Paula Heelan grew up in Tasmania. from The University of Queenslanc remote cattle station in the highlan. with her husband Peter. From the start, Paula loved the outback – the extraordinary people, the extreme weather, the challenges, the beauty and even teaching her two children, Matt and Ali, through distance education. She writes and takes photos with a focus on rural and remote Australia for a range of state, national and international publications. *Australian Midwives* is Paula's first book.

AUSTRALIAN MIDWIVES

PAULA HEELAN

First published March 2016 by Harlequin Nonfiction
An imprint of Harlequin Enterprises (Australia) Pty Ltd.
Level 13, 201 Elizabeth St
SYDNEY NSW 2000
AUSTRALIA

ISBN 978 176037198 2

AUSTRALIAN MIDWIVES
© Paula Heelan 2016

Cataloguing-in-Publication details are available from the National Library of Australia www.librariesaustralia.nla.gov.au

Cover design by Romina Panetta
Front cover image of midwife Chloe Coker by Kate Hannon, RFDS
Printed and bound in Australia by Griffin Press, South Australia

For Peter

CONTENTS

CHAPTER

1

Lane Johnson

Tasked with pilot Ben Ragg, known as Raggs, 26-year-old CareFlight nurse and midwife Lane Johnson was called out at three-thirty in the morning to pick up a woman on Groote Eylandt who had miscarried at 19 weeks pregnant. She was experiencing a postpartum haemorrhage (PPH) and had lost more than 800 millilitres of blood. Lane felt confident she could manage. 'Health staff at the clinic had stopped the bleeding, but the mother still needed to come to Darwin,' says Lane. She prepared for the flight and packed the drugs she thought might be needed as well as two units of blood. At 4 am Raggs lifted the King Air – an eight-person, two-stretcher, twin-engine turboprop aircraft – off the runway.

CareFlight is an aeromedical charity that provides rapid-response critical care. Aircrew, medical teams and coordinators deliver the best care they can as soon as possible – essentially bringing the right team to the right patient at the right time. Flight doctors and nurses transport medicine and care for injured patients who need emergency treatment at the scene of the incident. They also transport seriously ill patients and expectant mothers who need to be moved between clinics and hospitals.

With the very early morning start, Raggs and Lane were already tired. 'Halfway into the flight, Raggs, who's a very funny bloke, decided to keep me awake by telling me a joke,' Lane says.

'Have you heard the one about the goat? No? Well, there's a bloke sitting in a bar ...'

Distracted by a strong odour, Lane interrupted him. 'Raggs, can you smell that? I can smell smoke, a burning smell,' she said. Her heart skipped a beat when suddenly she heard a cold, mechanical breathing sound coming through the radio, like someone speaking through a scuba mask with a microphone in the regulator. 'I'm thinking, *What the hell?* I turned to see Raggs in the cockpit wearing a mask. He looked like Darth Vader out of *Star Wars*. I asked him if he was wearing an oxygen mask.'

'Phhrssffhhh, yes,' he breathed.

'I thought, *What? Where's mine?*'

'Phhsssfhhh,' came Darth's reply again. 'You don't get one.'

Lane looked wildly around to find Raggs hooked up to medical oxygen. Aware something was wrong, her heart was in her mouth. 'He looked like someone out of *Top Gun* on his own little pilot mission,' she says. 'Raggs never panics – he's as cool as a cucumber. But I could see he was clearly distressed by the burning smell. Later he told me he thought if we both became incapacitated it wouldn't be good, so that's why he put the giant oxygen mask on. I just didn't get one down the back.

I was terrified. Raggs figured out the heating element had burnt out and just needed to be switched off. Meanwhile, I'm down the back panicking away, thinking, *We might explode any second. I'm going to die on this plane.*' Raggs turned off the heating and checked with Lane whether or not the smell had gone. 'When I confirmed it had, he took his precious mask off.'

At that point, Raggs and Lane had arrived at Groote Eylandt, Australia's third-largest island with an archipelago that includes more than 40 smaller islands. On the western side of the Gulf of Carpentaria and about 640 kilometres south-east of Darwin, Groote Eylandt is the homeland of the Anindilyakwa people. The low-lying island measures about 50 kilometres from east to west and 60 kilometres north to south. A hilly island, it's coloured by extensive red plains, a rugged sandstone plateau, sand plains and savanna woodland dominated by stringybark eucalypts and Darwin woolly butt. There are patches of monsoon vine forest, pandanus and citrus pine, and Casuarina trees and Banyan figs give shelter and shade near the beaches.

They picked up the woman, who had been pregnant with her second baby. Raggs and Lane carefully placed her on board. She was still bleeding slightly, but her obs (observations) were fine and Lane didn't think she needed to give her blood. When she noticed the woman was clutching a tiny container with her deceased baby inside, she felt wretched. 'It was very impersonal and the sight of this poor woman holding it was very, very sad,' Lane says. While Lane and Raggs were settling the young woman on the plane, Lane received another call asking if she could pick up a woman at Ramingining – a community on the edge of the Arafura Swamp in Arnhem Land with a population of about 800. 'The woman had gone into early labour at 22 weeks. As we were the only aeromedical team flying in the Territory at that time, we didn't have a lot of choice and we were only about an hour away.' Lane checked with her patient, who was stable and okay, if she minded a small detour to pick up the Ramingining woman. After her own traumatic birth hours before, the woman said she just wanted to sleep. So Raggs and Lane flew into Ramingining, where they picked up the woman who was expecting her seventh child. She wasn't contracting and had been given drugs to calm the labour. In the early-morning darkness, they quietly loaded her safely on board.

With everyone secure and strapped in, Raggs took off. The plane was still climbing when suddenly the pregnant woman reached behind to where Lane was sitting and dug her nails into Lane's arm. 'I'm pushing!' she screamed. Lane grabbed the microphone to tell Raggs what was happening and to ask when she could undo the seatbelt and get up. With the aircraft still in a 45-degree climb, Raggs asked her to wait 30 seconds. Gripped with anxiety, she waited and waited and held the woman's hand, telling her she was doing well and to breathe, just breathe through it. When Raggs gave the okay to unbelt, Lane whipped up and knelt down beside her patient. As the small area at the back of the aircraft only takes two stretchers lying down – one on each side – there was very little room to move.

'The woman had opened her legs and I could see a bulging sack of fluids discharging. I was down the back and too far from the two-way mic to be able to relay information to Raggs. I thought, *Oh my God, this is not happening*.' She raced back up to the area behind the cockpit to grab her drug bag and neonatal bag valve mask (BVM), which is a hand-held device used to provide positive pressure ventilation to patients who are not breathing adequately. With only a small birthing bag kept on board for emergencies, Lane worried that she didn't have any of the regular birthing equipment like a neonatal cot or even a simple hand-held neopuff automatic ventilator. The first patient's baby had died and Lane hadn't expected to have to deal with the actual birth of a baby. Frightened about what might unfold, her hands were shaking. She tapped Raggs firmly on his shoulder. He turned to her and took off his mic. Above the roar of the engines, she yelled, 'I think we're about to have a baby, you need to fly faster.'

Lane returned to her patient and plugged in the oxygen. She had her neonatal BVM and drew up the drugs in preparation for the mum. Within minutes the woman pushed out the baby. Being tiny, it was still enclosed in the gestational sack that hadn't burst.

Just seconds after the birth, the sack popped. And there, in front of her, was a beautiful little boy. Lane rested him in her hand. He reached from the tip of her fingers down to her wrist-watch. She could see the baby was gasping for air and she needed to think level-headedly about what to do next. 'His arms and legs were in a starfish position and he seemed to be trying to close his hands to cover himself. He was vigorous and very much alive. I clamped and cut the cord.'

The plane was unusually cold because Raggs had had to turn off the heating system. Lane anxiously searched around for something warm to wrap the baby in. She found a plastic bag and swathed him in it. He was still gasping for air. So sitting cross-legged on the aircraft floor with the baby in her lap, Lane began ventilating him, giving him slight breaths. 'His mum looked over lovingly and cooed at her baby,' Lane recalls. 'I explained to her that he was very, very tiny, but he was alive.' Suddenly, the mother let Lane know she felt like pushing again. 'I placed the baby, still in the plastic bag, carefully on her chest and said she could have a little cuddle while I just took care of her.' The mother pushed out the placenta without any problems, and while very small, it looked complete.

Lane now checked the baby. His breathing was distressed and his dark skin had turned pale blue. His arms, which had previously been stretched above his head, and his legs, which had been bent at angles with muscles tensed, were now lifeless. His pint-sized chest was heaving. With her own heart racing, Lane sat down again and tried to BVM him. 'I started to ventilate him in my lap – by trying to force air into his alveoli in the lungs to inflate them. His chest became barrelled from using every single muscle, pronouncing his ribs with each chest movement. I gently squeezed a little orange bubble, no bigger than my fist, to blow air in from the BVM to his immature lungs using the pressure of two fingers. I had to get it exactly right: too small a squeeze and not enough air goes in, too much and you can over-inflate and burst a lung. I could see he was working hard to breathe.'

The roar of the plane's engine made using a stethoscope useless, so Lane balanced the baby on her lap and with two fingers still squeezing the BVM bulb, she slid her other hand into the plastic bag and placed two fingers over the apex of his chest and attempted to count the beats of his thumping heart. 'My attempt to multi-task meant my ventilation was ineffective, so I stopped bagging him and focused on counting the heartbeats through his chest wall. Eighty beats per minute. He was okay. It wasn't great, but it wasn't the worst. Infants have ridiculously high heart rates. Anything below 100 requires you to breathe for them, anything below 60 beats per minute [BPM], which would be fine for an adult, requires CPR. When I thought another 30 seconds had passed I stopped to check his heart again. It wasn't good, so I started CPR chest compressions. With two fingers again, straight down the centre of his chest I started the sequence. He wasn't positioned on my lap firmly, so I sat flat on the floor and balanced him on one thigh with my two fingers on his sternum pounding into his miniscule chest. My other two fingers were back on the bulb of the BVM. Push, push, push, breathe; push, push, push, breathe. Over and over again.'

Next thing, the mother told Lane she felt really faint. She was bleeding profusely. Lane remembered she hadn't given her the intramuscular injection of Syntocinon she had prepared. This is a synthetic replication of the hormone oxytocin which should occur naturally to stimulate the uterus to contract shortly after the baby is born to prevent bleeding. Lane could see clearly the mother needed the synthetic dose. 'I'd been so distracted by the baby, I hadn't followed protocol.' Running on adrenaline and dealing with each situation as it occurred as best she could, she turned her attention back to the mother. 'I had nowhere to put the little baby. He still had a gigantic oxygen mask over his face, which was the smallest we had on board. He was still in the garbage bag, so I wrapped him again in the biggest blanket I could find and placed him on a bundle of rugs on the back seat with the oxygen mask lying over his face and just had to leave him there.'

Lane injected the drug into the mother's leg and rubbed her stomach to try to stimulate the uterus to begin clamping down. 'But it wasn't clamping and I couldn't stop the blood from hosing out,' says Lane. 'I was at a total loss. I drew up some more Syntocinon, put it in a bag and started hanging it.' She checked the mother's blood pressure to find it was 42 over 38. Not good. Then she reached for the second blood unit she had brought on board for the first patient and gave it to the bleeding woman. After giving the blood and with the second dose of Syntocinon gone through the bag, the bleeding eventually slowed down. 'Her blood started to trickle rather than pour,' says Lane. 'I got my bearings and had a quick look at my first patient. She was okay, still sleeping. The second patient was now looking a little bit better after receiving blood and fluid. Everything that could be done was done.'

Lane reached for the baby, still lying on the back seat, and sat down on the floor next to the mother's legs and began CPR again. Suddenly, she became aware of the seatbelt sign – Raggs was recycling the seatbelt sound alert to grab her attention. She climbed into the back seat, carefully holding onto the baby, and managed to buckle her belt. Then she resumed compressions on the infant. She looked across at the two women: one was sleeping and the baby's mum was looking okay.

With the plane on a tilt for the landing, Lane could see the runway straight ahead from where she was seated up the back. Feeling overwhelmed, she started to cry. 'I thought, *Oh my God, I haven't called anyone and I haven't got any help coming.* I hadn't called our logistics team to tell them our arrival time or asked for help, or for paramedics to meet us – nothing.' It was 6 am when they landed and there was no one in sight. She was shattered. Raggs shut down the plane and all of a sudden the rumbling of the engines she had been constantly hearing fell silent.

Then, from a corner of the airport, two ambulances sped over and the most senior CareFlight doctor and staff members emerged. For the entire flight, Raggs had been relaying on the satellite phone to CareFlight all he could see happening down the back of the aircraft.

'I had completely forgotten to communicate with him,' Lane recalls. 'But he could see I was struggling. He knew I was performing CPR on the baby, giving blood, injecting Syntocinon

– he was totally on the ball and had relayed everything. At six o'clock that morning, everyone I needed appeared. The staircase door dropped open and the doctor was standing there. Senior doctors rarely meet a plane.' He looked at Lane with assurance and asked what he could do.

'You need to take this,' she managed to say and handed him the baby. The doctor carefully took the tiny bundle with the BVM from her arms.

'Yep, no worries,' he replied in a soothing voice. He whisked the baby away, accompanied by another nurse in the first ambulance. Before he left, he turned to Lane and asked if she would be okay with the two women. 'Yes, I'm fine,' she said, feeling the enormous weight lifting from her shoulders.

Raggs opened the cargo door and together they carefully unloaded each of the women. As they pulled the stretchers out in the pale, early-morning light, they could see how much blood had been lost. It had splashed up the sides of the walls and all over the floor. 'It had been so dark, I hadn't seen it,' Lane says. She had spent a large part of the flight sitting and working in a growing pool of blood. 'We got the women into the ambulance and the paramedics, who were just beautiful, suggested I take a little breather. *We'll load them on and take care of the blood pressures*, they said.'

Raggs took the moment to approach Lane and wrap her in his arms, telling her what a great job she'd done. Standing there, bathed in soft, orange sunrise, he decided they should have a photo together to remember their good work – everyone had made it alive. 'We have a beautiful photo of us from that horrendous morning that we'll never forget,' Lane says through tears of deep emotion.

The paramedic approached Lane and put a hand on her shoulder. It had just been radioed in that the first ambulance had had to pull over to try to intubate the premature baby boy on the way to the hospital. But the smallest tube they had to try to insert into the trachea to provide a definitive airway and maximise the effectiveness of resuscitation, was still too big. The baby was just too small. He had died. Lane was devastated.

But it wasn't yet over for Lane, and she had to work hard to hold herself together. She and the two paramedics moved the baby's mum across to the ambulance. Then as they were bringing the first patient over, Lane noticed she had started to bleed again. 'There was blood all over her,' she recalls. 'We started giving her the other remaining unit of blood.' With dread Lane realised that had she bled significantly in flight, it could have gone unnoticed with all her attention on the birth, the bleeding mother and the struggling baby. Now the initial patient was haemorrhaging. The medical team stabilised her, then climbed into the ambulance and sped off to the hospital. 'The mother didn't know at that stage that her baby had passed away. We got the two women to the resuscitation area, and although they both needed a little time in the intensive care unit, both mums survived.'

Though saving the mums was a wonderful outcome, the loss of the babies was something that would be felt by the whole community. When an Aboriginal family member passes away, the family belongs to everyone in the community and the sorrow is shared through kinship ties. Grief, known as 'sorry business', is shared by crying together, creating a communal sorrow and breaking the grief. On their return to their communities, each of the women and their families would receive lots of loving support led by the community's senior women. When it comes to the loss of a premature baby, the grieving is done in a more private, close family way – unlike the way it is done for older people, where a large, community ceremony is held.

Saving the two women depended as much on pilot Ben Ragg as it did on Lane. Ben began flying gliders in 1997 when he was only fifteen, and moved to powered aircraft in 2000. Set on a career as a pilot, he worked determinedly for several years to save the $100,000 needed for a pilot's licence, with qualifications to fly a commercial plane in bad weather. In the lead-up to full-time work as a commercial pilot, he towed gliders, flew skydivers and spent twelve months with Broome Air Services in Western Australia flying people around the Kimberley and Pilbara regions.

Ben soon landed a job with Chartair in Darwin and, based on his bush experience, was sent on his own with an aircraft to Ngukurr, a remote Aboriginal community on the banks of the Roper River in southern Arnhem Land, to start up a new base to fly patients to Katherine for medical appointments. Then, after several years with Hardy Aviation flying tradies, teachers, politicians, mining staff, medical crew, supermarket staff – anyone with a need to travel, to anywhere they needed to be – Ben started working for CareFlight in 2011. After two and a half years he was promoted to a supervising role to mentor new pilots for the first few months before they fly solo. 'All our flying is usually done with a single pilot,' he says. 'The training and mentoring was a strong area of interest for me, having lost two acquaintances and two work colleagues to preventable plane crashes.'

When Ben and Lane were tasked to the second patient, CareFlight base crew wanted to ensure Lane was happy with the first patient before loading her up with a second. 'A miscarriage at 22 weeks is a terrible thing for any parent to have to go through and it's also hard on the medical crew – they're just sad flights to be on,' Ben says. 'And it's certainly not the sort of job you want to be on when they ask if you can go to another 22-week pregnancy with a strong potential of miscarriage. Because we weren't leaving for the second patient from a larger centre, we didn't have a doctor or the extra equipment we'd normally take to a high-risk pregnancy. But Lane and I were the only crew that could get to the patient within the next five hours and likely to have her in a hospital within two.'

The fumes event happened when Ben and Lane were on their way to retrieve the first patient. 'Lane had asked me if I could make the cabin warmer than normal for her patient. Ninety-nine per cent of the time nothing goes wrong with the plane, and while we're busy, there's plenty of opportunity to chat – yes, we can do two things at once!' He laughs. 'But that all changes if we get a red light on the annunciator panel or someone tells us something isn't right – and that's what happened that night.'

'Smoke' is one of those words that will capture a pilot's full attention – and is treated as a real emergency. 'Much like the medical crew uses DRSABCD [which stands for Danger, Response, Send for help, Airway, Breathing, CPR, Defibrillator] and recognises that danger to themselves is initially more important than trying to help the patient's airway, breathing, circulation and so on, we have an aviation equivalent. Pilots need to make sure they are safe before attempting to fix the problem. Passing out from the smoke or fumes does nobody any good. Pilots have died trying to fix a simple problem – leaving nobody flying the plane to keep them or anyone else safe on board. From there we need to work out whether the smoke is electrical and smells like bacon, or from the environmental system, which is usually oil burning and smells like a cross between dirty socks and vomit. Either way, our world just got busy and we don't have time to chat.

'Electrical smoke gives me thirty things to do, environmental smoke only fifteen,' Ben continues. 'Neither involves dropping the passenger oxygen masks. Where there's smoke, there's fire and adding a lot of oxygen to fire is not a good thing. The passenger masks aren't anything like the pilot masks – they don't provide enough oxygen to overcome the fumes, so we don't deploy them. If they deploy automatically, it's actually the one time we tell people not to use them.' High above Groote Eylandt and aware he had just turned up the heater, Ben ran through the environmental checklist. 'I was also working out the nearest place I could get the aircraft on the ground – not all our day strips are useable at night,' he says. 'But before too much more had happened Lane mentioned the smell had gone – and suddenly we were back to a normal, uneventful flight and able to land at our planned destination.'

When Ben and Lane landed Ben thought the condition of the patient wasn't as serious as Lane had described. 'At 22 weeks the baby bump is barely showing and Indigenous women tend to be very quiet in labour. From the similar jobs I'd had in the past, I wrongly assumed this would be a quiet, uneventful flight back to Darwin. I should have realised no flights with Lane are uneventful,' he quips.

When Lane asked Ben if she could unbuckle her seatbelt after take-off and he asked her to wait 30 seconds, he didn't think she was too panicked at that stage. 'It's not unusual for the nurses to want to get back to work as soon as it's safe,' he says. 'I didn't realise that that would be the last time she'd put her headset on for the entire flight. We normally set up our planes so the more critical patient is on the front stretcher and the relatively well patient is on the rear stretcher. The exception to this is the midwifery jobs – nurses usually prefer to have pregnant women on the rear stretcher where there's more room in case there's a birth. Because that's not a very

common situation, the nurses don't normally have their head-
sets plugged in when they're down the back.'

Immediately after departure, pilots are very busy and it
wasn't until Lane tapped Ben on the shoulder and said *I think
we're about to have a baby* that he comprehended something
was going on. 'The nurses are ordinarily very good at keeping
us in the loop. When they're not, it's usually not very good.
I shouted back and asked if she wanted me to let anyone in
Darwin know – I don't think she heard me and she didn't talk
to me again,' he says.

Ben thought it was better to be safe than sorry and called
the logistics team on the sat phone and suggested they wake
up everyone. 'Even as a pilot, we know a pregnancy less than
24 weeks is very rarely viable, but the medical crew does everything it can until the woman reaches the hospital.

'About half an hour into the flight the woman birthed the
baby – worst possible scenario. There's very little we can really
do except get to a hospital as quickly as we can. I know that
first half hour is a trial of life for the baby – the more medical help it receives at that point, the more likely it is to make
it. I made another sat-phone call to keep logistics (and doctors on the ground) in the loop – the information can change
whether they bring a second ambulance to the airport or not.
I also called Air Traffic Control to let them know we'd gained
an extra passenger in flight as they need to know if there's an
accident – and it's good to confuse controllers at five in the
morning as to how we picked up someone in flight,' Ben says
with a laugh.

About twenty minutes out from Darwin Ben noticed things
weren't fine. 'Lane was in a pool of blood on the floor of the
aircraft performing CPR on the baby – while paying a lot of
attention to his mum at the same time. I twigged something

was wrong there as well so I gave logistics another call. The consultants, which are the most senior doctors, are pretty good at interpreting pilot-speak to work out what's going on – they also tend to go straight for the worst-case scenario. We had the former medical director on that night and it was the first time I'd heard him say, *I'm driving in now – I'll meet you at the plane*. This was from a pilot's description of events only – almost always they ask to be put on to the nurse or registrar.'

At two minutes to land, Ben could see Lane was still sitting in a pool of blood. 'We're required to have passengers wear a seatbelt and I'd given up shouting long ago. I cycled the seat-belt sign a couple of times, which sounds like a chime – it was enough to get Lane's attention and I pointed to the runway. We can keep flying if the nurses need more time, but the look on Lane's face at seeing the runway and jumping back into the escort's seat told me she was ready for this to be over – and time for me to get the plane on the ground.'

After the ordeal hospital staff surrounded Lane. 'They were literally patting me on the back, telling me what a good job I had done,' she says with surprise. 'Everyone was really amaz-ing. They kept bringing me cups of tea and asking if I was hun-gry. The senior doctors came in to chat and to ask what had happened and what I'd done. They told me I'd done an amaz-ing job.' But despite the unremitting praise, Lane was over-whelmed with concern. Was it the best she could have done? 'If I'd given the drugs straightaway, maybe the mother wouldn't have bled? And then I would've had more time with the baby. I had to accept that it was just one of those things that can hap-pen when there are so few resources to work with.'

With everyone showing great concern and care for her, this somehow made it worse for Lane that morning. The experi-ence of that disastrous night had definitely upset her. She went home to her apartment. It wasn't until she walked through her front door that she noticed she was covered in blood. She stripped off her blood-soaked uniform and dumped it in the outside bin.

She crawled into bed and fell into a deep sleep. 'I had had a big cry at the hospital and was exhausted,' she says. 'When I woke up at home, my arms were cradled. I thought I was still holding the baby. It was so vivid. It was horrific to wake up that afternoon thinking he was still in my arms and then to remember that he'd died.'

Lane rolled over and reached for her phone, which sat on the side table. There was a message from Raggs. It read: *So about that goat*, and he finished the joke. 'It made me feel so much better. It just capped off that long, traumatic morning that had started with the stupid fire scare on board,' she says. 'At the hospital they refer to that day as the disaster night and use it as an example of what can go wrong when teaching student nurses. I was very lucky to have had such a supportive team and Raggs was just spectacular. That's the only way to describe him. The senior doctor racing out and taking the baby from my arms, the support from paramedics and hospital staff – everyone was just at the top of their game. It was incredible.'

Having to cope with that kind of catastrophic, extreme incident by yourself in the middle of the night on a small plane doesn't happen often. 'Usually, we get a heads-up about what we're going to do and can decide what equipment we need and how many hands to take. We can take a doctor or a specialist with us if we think it's necessary.'

Lane had thought one woman bleeding was totally within her manageable scope of practice. 'I would have taken a doctor, a neonatal cot and a heating chamber and some extra bits and pieces had I known what was going to unfold. You can't predict these things. I went back into work that afternoon to debrief. Everyone came in after their night shift in their own time to talk and find out what had happened. When we went through it, I was very open about the fact that I had felt I'd failed to give the drug soon enough and that this may have led to the catastrophic haemorrhage. People were very sweet and understood I had just been caught up with a little baby boy that had pulled at my heartstrings – he was a massive distraction in the course of my work. They talk about this in emergency work – it's known as "scene distraction". In the end, you just do the best you can.'

After the debrief Lane felt better. Everyone echoed again what a professional job she had done, and while some may have taken different steps, they might not have been able to do as much. 'I crammed a lot into the relatively short flight of one hour and ten minutes from Ramingining to when I saw that runway in Darwin. It felt like ten minutes.'

Lane turned up to the CareFlight office for work the next day without realising how shaken she still was. She was sent home and after a good night's rest, she felt better and was back on the job the following day. But two years later, she still thinks about that night. 'This is the first time I've cried about it since then,' she says. 'You can be a little blasé when it comes to protecting yourself. I haven't gone into so much detail about it since it happened. I guess that's the self-preservation strategy at work. If you burst into tears every time you talk about a difficult experience, you'll crack. And it wasn't my journey – it was the journey of the women in my care and their babies. I was just there to help.'

Lane grew up on Sydney's north shore with her parents and two younger brothers. In 2008, armed with a Bachelor of Nursing, she began working at Sydney's Hornsby Ku-ring-gai Hospital in the emergency department where she had trained. She also completed her postgraduate training in critical care. 'My training covered everything, but I really just loved the blood and guts,' she admits. 'I had always known I would. Growing up I loved playing doctors and nurses with my brothers. Charming children that we were – often caught running around with kitchen knives and scissors, playing operations.'

Lane gathered and built skills in resuscitation, triage (prioritising injured people when limited medical resources are available in an emergency), ordering her own bloods and X-rays. 'Working in emergency is great for gaining knowledge because there's constantly something new coming through. It's one of those places where the more you learn, the more you realise how little you know. I was completely under the wings of senior nurses until I moved to the Manly Hospital's emergency department in 2011. Going in with a fresh slate at Manly was really nice. At last I wasn't known as the baby nurse in training. Instead, I went in as one of the more senior staff.'

At Manly, Lane provided continuity of care for pregnant women. She did the antenatal appointments and was on call to attend the births of the babies of the women in her care. She also followed through with the postnatal care. 'As a student it helps to follow the woman's journey and it's helpful for the woman to form a bond and trust in her midwife. It's a model that's been proven to reduce maternal stress and can lead to a better birthing experience emotionally.'

Lane was following a patient named Katherine at Manly. Along the way it had been a normal, uneventful pregnancy with a scheduled caesarian. 'Everything was going to plan and a beautiful, term baby girl, named Laura, was born,' Lane says. 'While Katherine was still on the operating table we gave the baby a little wash and brought her to her proud parents for cuddles. Two minutes later Katherine said, *Lane, I don't think she's breathing.* Sure enough the baby had dropped like a sack of potatoes. I grabbed her and raced her back to the Resuscitaire [the neonatal resuscitation station]. Her heart was beating but she wasn't breathing. My supervisor, Karen, swiftly gave positive pressure ventilation with the neopuff. Thirty seconds later we checked again and found there was no heartbeat. I started CPR and before we knew it we were a team in high action. A surgeon helped and after quite the emergency, Laura was revived and well. I nicknamed her Spud because she had dropped like a sack of potatoes without warning. She had scared us half to death – not least her mother. The family put a lovely thankyou letter in the local paper, which I kept.'

Three years later, Lane was visiting Sydney – for only the third time since she'd left for Darwin. 'I was walking along a main road with a girlfriend when next minute, a car pulled up beside us – completely stopping the traffic. A woman yelled out – *Hey, are you a midwife?* It was Katherine – she had circled the block three times checking to see if it was me. She was screaming out the car window – still holding up the traffic – and in front of all the onlookers called out, *You did CPR on my baby – you're my angel. I've got Spud in the back seat! I knew it was you, Lane – I'd never forget that smile.* She pulled up and we had a great chat and I got to meet three-year-old Spud. It was one of the most humbling moments of my life.'

Lane had longed to become a flight nurse since she saw a Royal Flying Doctor Service (RFDS) stand at the Sydney Royal Easter Show. That was it. That was her dream. After two years at Manly in the emergency department, she decided to study midwifery to increase her chances of becoming an aeromedical flight nurse. 'I hated it at first,' she admits. 'I found it hard because it was so women-centred. There are a lot of very strong personalities in midwifery and everyone has their own style, agenda and beliefs. Some believe in pain relief, some don't, some love bouncy balls, others water births. I found spending long hours with women who really need you while they are in labour, intensive. I was just there for the skills I needed to become a flight nurse, not so much the midwifery.'

When Lane got the job as CareFlight nurse and midwife in 2012, she packed her bags and flew out of Sydney. She arrived in Darwin with very little idea about what lay ahead. 'With a population of 127,000 the city is quite small and there are no department stores like David Jones or Myer,' she says. 'There are no four seasons – it just has a wet season and a dry season and you just get used to the year-round tropical humidity. It's a great outdoors place with plenty of fishing, walking and swimming and there's a great mix of people – it's very multicultural.'

While Lane was over the moon about the job, it was a very steep learning curve because she had never worked as a sole practitioner before. 'When you fly up here, it's usually just you and a pilot. I found it nerve-racking at first and was pretty much overwhelmed with it all. But the pilots are extremely professional and astute and try their best to assist new crew. They pick up quickly on things and assist whenever they can.'

During her first two weeks in Darwin, despite her anxieties, Lane embraced all things new with fierce determination. The first day she stepped onto a King Air plane she was on a 'buddy flight' with the nurse on duty. This is a training flight for new nurses under the supervision of an experienced, senior nurse. They had been assigned to retrieve an ill patient and Lane was terrified. 'At that stage I was just along for the ride to watch how the nurse interacted with clinic staff and patients.'

Not long after she started working on her own, she stepped off the plane into the red dust of the remote community of Wadeye (pronounced wod-air-yer) and was driven from the air-strip into the middle of the settlement. As the four-wheel-drive-cum-outback-ambulance hurtled along, Lane noticed countless camp dogs and idle young men sheltering under trees and door-ways from the searing sun. The vehicle pulled into a secure steel structure next to the clinic. The bumper sticker read, *No Hum-bugging*, meaning 'don't annoy the clinic staff – no free rides'.

Wadeye, also known as Port Keats, has grown to become one of the largest remote Indigenous communities in the Northern Territory with a population of more than 2500 people. Iso-lated, it sits on the Indian Ocean and the western edge of the Daly River Reserve, 420 kilometres south-west of Darwin. Dur-ing the wet season the roads are cut for about five months of the year from heavy rain and movement is restricted to travel by air or sea. Wadeye is in the Thamarrurr Region, home to three ceremonial groups, at least five languages and four dia-lects. Languages include Murrinhpatha, Marri Ngarr, Murrinh Nuwayn, Marri Tjevin, and Ngangi Tjemerri. Murrinhpatha is the most commonly spoken, though it may be a person's sec-ond or third language. English is not widely spoken and is used mostly to communicate with non-Indigenous people.

Lane walked courageously towards the medical clinic. She tried to look confident. The expectant mum and her family would be depending on her. But she was nervous. She didn't know what to anticipate and she worried she mightn't be up to the task. She would be the only health professional with midwifery skills within an hour's flight of this remote place.

As she swung open the clinic door, everyone was gathered waiting for her. Their faces looked up at her keenly, relief on each one. 'Thank God you're here!' exclaimed the health worker.

Lane's heart sank. 'I thought, *I'm not telling them this will be my first independent birthing experience,*' she says. But instinctively she clicked into gear, putting all her training into practice. The mother was eight centimetres dilated, but everything else seemed fine. After an hour and no progress made due to the mother's dehydration, Lane made the decision to commence intravenous (IV) fluids and happily, before long and without fuss, the woman gave birth to a beautiful little girl. 'It was a lovely, analgesic-free, natural birth and one of the most amazing experiences I've ever had,' says Lane. 'It was certainly the best first job I could've asked for – a lucky start to my professional midwifery career, and I often think back to that perfect, natural birth.'

With her Sydney-based training, where it was all about the importance of natural birthing and encouraging skin-to-skin contact between mother and baby, Lane wasn't prepared for the plethora of women that was outside the clinic waiting for the women's business to unfold. 'Seconds after the placenta was passed they came streaming in to see the new family addition. At just minutes old, the baby was passed around for cuddles and photos with nearly a dozen family members.' Lane and the pilot flew the mother and her tiny baby back to Darwin for a full check-up and later the pair returned to Wadeye on a commercial flight.

For the next few months Lane attended mostly trauma and emergency jobs, rather than midwifery cases, until one day she got a call-out to a pregnant woman who had gone into early labour. 'Clinic staff told us she'd missed the bus to the hospital in Katherine and we needed to fly her to Darwin. We arrived and I examined her, but despite being told the contractions were one in ten or fifteen minutes, I couldn't feel any. We got her onto the plane and into the air and I asked her if she was having any labour signs.

'*Ahww, I'll be honest with you, Sister. I'm not in labour. There's no Kmart in town.* She didn't want to take the bus to Katherine to have her baby because her other five children needed clothes and they're much cheaper in Kmart. We were in the air and decided to keep going. I gave her a magazine. My work was done.'

Darwin has a wet season and a dry season. With the wet comes storms, pounding winds and cyclones, and the dry season brings bushfires, dust storms and fog. 'Flying up here is constantly a challenge for our pilots,' Lane says. 'Even if we can get to a destination, it's another thing whether or not we can land. There are often obstacles on runways like dingoes, foxes, feral pigs, horses and cattle, or the airstrip lights might be broken and we can't see where to land. Sometimes if people are intensely sick and we can't land in their community, we ask if someone can drive them to another place where we might be able to land. That could mean a two- to three-hour drive over a corrugated dirt road. As well as calling into lots of remote communities, we often fly into cattle stations,' Lane adds. 'Ideally, their airstrips are well maintained. They need to be the right length and width and have the right ground and lights for us to land safely.'

One night after a very large storm and significant rain in Darwin, Lane received a call-out to retrieve a woman from a large community. The woman waiting for the pick-up was 37 weeks pregnant and had suffered a concealed haemorrhage – the placental lining had separated from the uterus wall before delivery. Together with pilot Matt Mommers, known to his colleagues as Mommers, Lane's task was to take a neonatologist – a specialist doctor from Royal Darwin Hospital who treats newborn and premature infants – along with them and to bring the woman to Darwin. The CareFlight team briefed the doctor and they left at 8 pm on a King Air plane. When they arrived at the clinic after the 30-minute drive from the airstrip, Lane was surprised to find the woman up having dinner and walking around. 'We'd been given a much grimmer picture of her condition over the phone,' says Lane. 'She was able to walk across to the plane with us. But the weather was very bad in Darwin and it was raining significantly across the region. Mommers told us we couldn't fly. So we sat at the airfield and waited. Our patient watched TV and I spent the time monitoring the baby and listening to the heartbeats. Everything was fine.'

About 40 minutes later Mommers said the weather had improved in Darwin. The line of storms had passed, but there was still low cloud and heavy rain forecasted with occasional thunderstorms until daybreak. 'He said we'd be good to go,' Lane says. 'By now it was nearly midnight and in a typical wet season it was still raining, stinking hot and sticky.' The crew and the patient were weary. During the flight Mommers, who is generally a chatterbox with an incessant wide grin spread across his face, was very quiet. Lane could see he was working hard to fly through the storms. 'Lightning was flashing on both sides of us and the cabin was lighting up like a disco. Violent jabs were tossing us about, up and down, left and right.' Thinking she could lighten the mood, Lane asked Mommers if he'd like the Curly Wurly chocolate she had in her pocket.

'No, I do not want a Curly Wurly,' he replied gruffly.

'He was flying very hard and he was not happy,' Lane says. 'He was flying that plane the best he could. To my disbelief our patient and the specialist were sleeping through it. I thought, *I'm standing guard, no worries everyone.*'

About 75 kilometres from Darwin Mommers broke the news to Lane that they wouldn't be able to land.

'What?' she asked.

'I can't land here,' he said. 'I can't see the runway. We're going to have to go back.' Heavy thunderstorm activity, drenching rain and low cloud were a big concern. The storms were developing over Darwin airport and Mommers knew it wasn't safe to attempt a landing approach. 'In weather conditions like this the aircraft carries 60 minutes of holding fuel to allow the weather to pass through,' Mommers explains. 'And that was the case that night. If I had penetrated a thunderstorm like that, I would've risked injury to us from the severe turbulence and also the potentially catastrophic damage to the aircraft. They're not designed to handle the violent updrafts and downdrafts in the middle of a thunderstorm.'

Watching the radar, it didn't look like the weather was going to dissipate anytime soon. 'I had two options,' Mommers says. 'The first was to fly to a small community – a ten-minute flight from Darwin – or divert back to where we'd picked up our patient. The smaller place, a remote Indigenous community, wouldn't have had any medical assistance on hand for the mum or Lane. It would've been no better than the baby birthing in the plane. I had to make the call early so I'd still have enough fuel to conduct two instrument approaches – that's what you do in bad weather to get down to a low level. We were holding for about 40 minutes and I calculated that if we diverted back to the larger community we'd come from, I'd still have enough fuel for three instrument approaches if the weather was bad.'

As they flew back towards the town they'd just left, storm clouds were chasing them. They were flying through extremely heavy rain and turbulence and ice was accumulating on the airframe. An ice build-up can be very dangerous in some circumstances and occasionally means the plane has to descend into warmer air. The aircraft was getting thrown about. Lane was worried. 'I could see a St Elmo's fire – a blazing light show on the edge of the propellers and along the wing tips.' A St Elmo's fire is a rare phenomenon that can occur through electrical build-up when an aircraft is near a thunderstorm. The specialist was woken by a thud and Lane told him they couldn't get back to Darwin. She could see the disappointment sinking in.

The landing approach was clear and smooth, until suddenly a wild gust of wind picked up the plane and thumped it back on the ground, shaking the crew violently. 'The patient looked up at me in alarm. *I think my waters just broke*,' she said.

'I got on the intercom and told Mommers his landing was so hard, he had broken the patient's waters.' He turned to Lane and with a look of relief at having landed the plane and with the smile almost back on his face he said, 'I'll take a raincheck on the Curly Wurly.'

When the plane had stopped Lane looked under the blanket covering the patient to find her covered in blood. It was not good. Lane had begun a vaginal examination when moments later the stair door was flung open. Mommers was checking on her. 'Are you alright in there?'

'Get out, women's business,' Lane yelled urgently, knowing her patient would not want a male nearby. The woman told Lane she was in a fair bit of pain. 'I know, it's okay, we'll sort it. Take some deep breaths,' Lane said to her with as much reassurance in her voice as she could muster. She called Care-Flight's logistics team. 'I think she's having a haemorrhage. She's bleeding and her stomach is rock hard. We need to do a caesarian,' Lane told the team.

'Luckily there was an anaesthetist in town,' Lane says. 'That was very unusual. The stars had aligned. But as we loaded the patient into the ambulance she started screaming blue murder. Her stomach pulled up to one side, like a basketball. She was screaming and afraid.'

Not able to give her any pain relief because of the apparent, imminent birth (drugs like morphine could relieve the mother's pain, but would cross the placenta and decrease the baby's ability to breathe and adapt to life outside the womb), Lane tried to calm her and explain what they were going to do. She assumed the placenta was at least partially off the wall of the womb, meaning the baby wouldn't be getting as much oxygen as it should. Still hours from a major hospital, Lane knew it was serious. 'Again, communities just pull together when things go wrong,' she says. Lane and the hastily assembled healthcare team wheeled the patient through to the theatre for an emergency caesarian. She had lost a lot of blood and Lane was worried. 'The baby came out a little floppy and had some breathing issues, but was okay. The neonatologist intubated the baby. As we had packed all our equipment in case of a worst-case scenario, everything turned out well.'

Lane was working to stabilise the baby when Mommers called in to the clinic to say he was sorry but he was out of flying hours and would have to leave without them. He'd managed to grab a couple of hours of sleep on the couch.

'Are you kidding me?' Lane asked.

'No, but someone will be back for you in the morning.'

Mommers flew the empty plane back to Darwin. As he landed, the day-shift pilot was taxiing out for take-off to pick up Lane and the doctor. Had Mommers waited for Lane, he would have acted against the Civil Aviation Safety Authority's (CASA) strict flying-hour rules. 'It was a lonely flight back,' he says.

'A strong part of the decision process that night was working out what was going to be best for the mother and baby,' Mommers says. 'In hindsight, we picked the better option. Had what happened to the mother occurred at the smaller community, Lane and I were certain she wouldn't have survived with that kind of blood loss. The medical resources required

wouldn't have been there. We were relieved she was able to go
to a place where she could be admitted to theatre.'

The next morning, the baby was stable and the mother out
of theatre. She wasn't stable enough to transfer because she'd
lost a lot of blood and when open surgery is performed, flying isn't recommended. She proudly held her baby while Lane
took some photos of the two of them together. 'Then we took
our super-cute passenger in a big crib with all our flash equipment safely back to Darwin. The mother was transferred later
that day to join her baby.'

Generally, up to about 36 weeks gestation, pregnant women
present to their local health clinic for antenatal care with a
resident or visiting midwife. After that time they take a bus or
vehicle, often over unsealed roads, to one of the smaller hospitals in the Northern Territory or to Darwin for their confine-
ment for the birth. The government assists with housing and
expenses while the mothers wait for their births. But all that is
against the Indigenous practice of having a natural birth on the
land their baby belongs to. 'Being away from family for up to
five weeks can be traumatic, particularly when you're in such
a vulnerable position,' Lane says. 'Unfortunately, it's not possible to put a high number of birth centres over the Territory's
vast expanse.'

A major part of Lane's work in the Northern Territory calls
on her ability to understand cultural differences in the remote
Aboriginal communities she works in. Delivering services to
Aboriginal families and communities can be complex. Social
problems can be deeply entrenched and historical, social, community, family and individual factors need to be considered.
Australian Indigenous cultures are not homogenous and communities differ widely. They often have characteristics specific
to geographic location and vary significantly to one another.

Many Indigenous families and communities face immense challenges, some of which contribute to high levels of poverty, unemployment, violence and substance abuse.

'I've learned about different cultures, languages, tribes and communities – it's a whole other world up here and one Sydney didn't prepare me for,' Lane says. 'I was completely ignorant of the issues when I arrived. I learned that women often have pregnancies with no antenatal care until they give birth. On the whole, pregnancy and birthing is sacred women's business. The men wait outside. The people have an incredibly strong connection with the land and are desperate to have their babies birthed on the land. They'll try to avoid coming into town to birth their babies. It's everyone's right – you should be able to have the birth you want. But sadly, we just don't have the resources to be able to support that.'

CareFlight senior flight nurse Jodie Mills says Lane is a joy to work with. 'We see her as the baby of the fleet,' she says, smiling. 'But her skills certainly don't represent that. She's an extremely talented nurse and midwife. Even though she seems to always get herself into hard situations with little neonate babies, her ability to deal with emergencies is exceptional. We have a running joke that if a neonate is going to come in, it'll be Lane that's on. But in saying that, she always conducts herself with the utmost professionalism and her competency in looking after the extreme neonate [24 to 25 weeks] is unquestionable. She works in exceedingly difficult situations where she doesn't have the luxury of being in a major hospital with a lot of support – 85 per cent of the time it's flight nurse only and she's on her own. Lane's extremely capable of handling that. She's an incredibly important part of our team and we're really proud of her at CareFlight.'

The very first time Lane helped birth a baby set the tone for her midwifery career. 'That plain-sailing, natural birth was a really moving experience. I feel very privileged to be involved in midwifery in remote communities and all the wonderful experiences that come with it. It's fantastic to be one of the very few people who often gets to coo and ahh over a newborn. Despite being a bit of a disaster magnet and known for it, I'm living the dream. I have a lovely boyfriend in Darwin. Joe is from Victoria and we met here. He recently decided to return to university to study biomedical science. He's a very smart man.'

Sitting in an egg chair on the deck of her apartment looking across the ocean, Lane says she loves Darwin's laidback way of life. 'It's totally different here and the fact that I get a glimpse into very sacred and ancient Aboriginal communities and have an opportunity to help improve the health and wellbeing of those living there is a great honour. I'm working in a vast, incredible part of Australia that most people never get to see.

'My midwifery career started as a huge task and undertaking. To think I dreaded the course and pretty much let everyone know I hated it! But now it's my favourite job. When I'm tasked to a midwifery case, I get excited. These days I'd much prefer to go to a beautiful birth than a roadside trauma. Blood and guts used to be my thing. But now I am loving midwifery. I am a midwife.'

2

Catherine (Kate) Austin

As Kate hurried to the health centre in a small community in the Victoria River District, 580 kilometres south-west of Katherine in the Northern Territory, she turned over in her mind the procedures she'd need to put in place for an upcoming birth. It was two in the morning and Kate had just had word that Mary's waters had broken. Not long in remote midwifery work, Kate was about to experience her first independent Indigenous birth – and she was a little on edge.

An experienced nurse, she had been providing antenatal care for Mary for the past few months and had organised an air transfer to a regional hospital for Mary's sit-down [her waiting time away from her community, usually between 37 and 38 weeks gestation] for later in the week. Mary was expecting her third child and Kate knew it could be a rapid birth. She also knew Mary had haemorrhaged following both previous births.

When Kate reached the clinic she found Mary wasn't yet in established labour. She did what she could to make her comfortable, recorded the necessary observations and phoned the aeromedical retrieval crew to reschedule the pick-up. Morning dawned, but still no baby. Nor had there been any indication of the aeromedical retrieval pick-up time to the hospital. Kate was well aware that for the safety of mother and baby it was preferable to get Mary to the hospital. 'Women are usually transferred pre-labour or after the birth for any necessary medical care,' Kate says. 'With no further signs of labour, Mary rested for the day with lots of family and friends popping in and out to visit her.'

West of the halfway point between Alice Springs and Darwin, the community is close to the centre of Australia in semi-arid country on the edge of the Tanami Desert, where the climate is hot and dry. It has an almost exclusively Aboriginal population of more than 800, and Warlpiri is the dominant language. Non-Indigenous people are the visiting service providers, including health-centre staff, teachers, police and council administrators. Despite the harsh, isolated setting, it was one Kate quickly embraced.

Late that afternoon the health centre doctor phoned the flight medical officer from Darwin, who didn't seem too concerned about the flight delay for Mary's retrieval. 'You have a midwife,' he said.

'At about 9 pm the aeromedical team finally phoned me with an estimated time of arrival of 11 pm,' Kate says. 'I thought, *That's great, now I can do the necessary paperwork and prepare for an evacuation.* There wasn't a bassinet or cot at the health centre, so while I was waiting I fashioned a crib by lining a little box with linen and placed it on the second bed in the emergency room in case it was needed.'

Suddenly, Mary began very strong labour contractions. Kate contacted the on-call nurse, Jennie, who although not a midwife was a mother of two. Kate knew she would be a great help. Jennie rushed in and asked Kate what she needed her to do. 'It was winter in the desert,' Kate says. 'And with no way to warm towels, I asked her to warm them in the laundry dryer outside. It was a bitterly cold night and we would have to keep the baby warm.'

A short time later, with quite a fast and uncomplicated birth, a healthy baby girl was born into Kate's hands. 'We were surrounded by supportive, loving grandmothers and aunties,' she says. 'It was a very happy occasion and I thought, *Thank goodness my first birth here has gone well.*'

But it wasn't over yet. Mary had low blood pressure and had lost a considerable amount of blood, although this didn't surprise Kate with Mary's birthing history. Kate contacted the medical evacuation team again and they gave an updated arrival time of 5 am. 'After breastfeeding her baby and having a short sleep, Mary wanted to have a shower,' Kate says. 'With the shower outside the health centre and on such a cold morning, we suggested she sit on a chair in front of the basin and have a nice warm wash.' But as Mary was sitting on the chair she began to feel very faint. 'Jennie was holding the baby and I called to her, *Quickly, put the baby in the box!* We laughed about my outburst later. I was glad I got to use my little makeshift crib. We helped Mary back to bed and ameliorated her symptoms from the blood loss. She recovered and when we heard the plane finally come in we transferred mother and baby to the airstrip.'

As it was one of the coldest nights Kate had experienced in the desert, she was quite concerned about her patients. 'While it only took the evacuation team a short time to prepare the loading mechanism for the stretcher, we were all feeling the cold. Safely at the hospital and with the help of a blood transfusion, Mary recovered without any problem.' By the time Kate finished in the emergency room it was after 6 am. She had been awake for 28 hours. 'I was very happy to have the next day off to recuperate,' she says. 'It was such a joy each time I went back into that community over the next twelve months to watch that little girl grow. It doesn't matter where a baby is born; it is always an incredibly special time.'

It was only in her wildest dreams Kate imagined that one day she'd be delivering babies in some of Australia's most remote places. Born in 1952, she grew up in south-east New South Wales on a large cattle property, Clear Springs Station, which her father managed. With her older sister, Jan, her childhood was idyllic. 'My parents had another two daughters, Margaret and Robin, quite a bit later and by the time the eldest was five, Jan and I had left for boarding school. Our parents gave us a lot of freedom and we were mad on our horses. My mother was a physiotherapist and a great naturalist. She knew flora and fauna very well. In 1953 my father had the property declared as a wildlife sanctuary, which meant no one could come shooting on the land without a permit and we shared it with the wildlife. My parents planted thousands of trees as plantation trees.'

With her mind set on a nursing career, Kate began her three-year training in 1969 at the Canberra Hospital. 'I aspired to several of the women in my family who had nursed here and overseas,' she says. 'When my maternal grandmother's male friends were heading off to the First World War, she sailed to England under her own volition and joined the Queen Alexandra's Imperial Medical Nursing Service Reserve (QAIMNS), where she became the matron of St David's hospital on Malta, one of the receival hospitals for the servicemen injured at Gallipoli. She died in 1918 on her way home.'

When she trained, Kate and her fellow nurses were all just seventeen years old and by the second year, at all of eighteen, they were often left in charge of a ward on night duty for eighteen to twenty patients. 'There weren't enough nurses, so they just let us loose. We, patients and nurses, were in the lap of the Gods!'

Kate thrived in this environment. On graduation, without a second thought, she eagerly chose obstetrics to work in maternity and children's nursing. And for six months after training she worked in a children's ward.

In 1973 the Tumbarumba Hospital (where her mother worked as a physiotherapist) was looking for a nurse to fill a casual vacancy. The 36-bed hospital was 480 kilometres south-west of Sydney and had an aged care and maternity unit. It was where Kate's first experience with assisting the birth of a baby unfolded.

'It was in the middle of the night and the midwife said to me, *Quickly, leg. Leg?* I asked. Then she told me to get up on the bed and hold the mother's leg up. That was in the days when midwives delivered babies with the mothers lying on their left side. So I did what I was told and jumped up on the bed and held up the leg. Then I had to jump back down to hold the baby as it birthed. And as I did, all the amniotic fluid ran down my uniform into my shoes. I wasn't quick enough, nor did I know it was a good idea to put on a long plastic apron before you jumped up on the bed and legged. I've remembered that clearly ever since – you don't do it twice.'

With Tumbarumba and district population at more than 3000, it was a busy little hospital. Understaffed and with only one doctor, it was an arduous job for Kate, who was on call following her shifts in case a transfer to Wagga Wagga was needed. 'As much as I loved the work, it was a bit out of control. It worried me that I couldn't really give people the amount of time I wanted to. After twelve months, I thought I needed to get back to study and midwifery was really what I wanted to do.' She enrolled for the course at the Royal Women's Hospital in 1974 in Melbourne, and while shifting from a small rural hospital to the city was hard because she wasn't a city girl, she loved the training.

Later that year Kate met Peter, who was studying at an agricultural college in Geelong. They married the following year, six months after Kate finished her midwifery training. They moved to Victoria's western district, where Kate worked in a few small hospitals and Peter became an overseer on a cattle-and-sheep property at Colac.

'Soon after we bought a farm at Mortlake, and in 1978 our daughter Penny was born,' Kate says. 'Belinda arrived in 1979, then Stuart in 1982 and Sal in 1986. In between having children I worked part-time as a midwife at a 30-bed busy little maternity unit at the Terang Hospital. Back then women stayed in hospital with their newborns for five days and rested. It was a lovely place to work. I even delivered a few friends' babies there. They just happened to come in when I was on duty. That was the nice thing about country nursing.'

Living in Victoria in the eighties was a punishing time for rural families. In 1982 Victoria was gripped by drought, and not long after in 1987 interest rates skyrocketed to eighteen per cent, making it impossible for people to make ends meet. 'We lived too far out of town for our children to attend school as day students, so we decided we had to change course,' Kate explains. 'Peter got a job with the stock-and-station-agent company Dalgety in Albury and we moved there. But after a while we were all desperate to get out of town again and move back to the country.'

From 1989 to 2009 Kate managed a small private health facility. In fact, according to Peter, Kate set up the first day-surgery business in southern New South Wales. 'When it was sold another group of practitioners bought it and built a new facility in Albury and Kate was charged with developing the new clinic in that building. There was a lot of planning involved and liaison with the Health Department. There are a lot of things Kate has done that the majority of nurses would never have been involved in,' Peter says. 'She gets in and makes things happen – she's highly experienced.'

Over that time Kate gained a postgraduate diploma in advanced nursing in rural health through La Trobe University in Wodonga. She also received a scholarship to complete a master's degree in nursing through the University of Newcastle. Her goal was to get back into rural or remote nursing and to work as a midwife.

In 2009 Kate left to join Aspen Medical's Remote Area Health Corps (RAHC). RAHC was initiated in 2008 to support the health workforce in remote Indigenous communities across the Northern Territory. It provides nurses, doctors and allied health professionals as primary healthcare providers for the shortfall in health-service delivery in remote communities.

At first, Kate was based at the Latchford Barracks, an Australian Army base in Bonegilla, east of Wodonga. Before long she obtained placements in remote Indigenous communities and was tasked to focus on children's and maternal health and midwifery. Her priority was (and still is) to raise the health profile of women and children in remote areas and she works determinedly to achieve this. 'My RAHC contract blocks range from three to six weeks in any one place,' she says. 'It took me a little while to learn the ropes and adjust to work in remote areas, but once I did I absolutely loved it.'

Kate has worked in myriad community clinics in the Northern Territory as a midwife and remote nurse, including Groote Eylandt, North East Arnhem, Croker Island, Oenpelli (Kakadu), Douglas Daly District, Maningrida and Milingimbi Island. The first remote community she stepped foot into was Lajamanu at Hooker Creek Station on the western desert of the Tanami in March 2010. The station had been taken over by the Aboriginal Land Council back in the 1980s and Lajamanu community was developed. Kate was flown in for a six-week stint. 'I soon became aware of just how short remote communities were of midwives,' she says. 'This was a terrific opportunity for me to get back into practising midwifery – and since then my work has involved 90 per cent mid.'

From 2009 to 2012, based in Albury, Kate flew out to the Territory to work and then in 2012 she and Peter moved to a property at Blackbutt, near Toowoomba in south-east Queensland. Kate now flies to work from Brisbane, a two-hour drive from the farm.

In 2011 Aspen Medical was contracted by the government to implement a program called the Nursing and Allied Health Rural Locum Scheme (NAHRLS) and Kate works for this program as well. 'The aim is to relieve nurses and allied health professionals in rural and remote areas while the local staff attend education programs,' Kate says. 'I work at health clinics and small country hospitals – wherever the need is.'

Working in remote areas is different to working in rural and regional hospitals and Kate has become very passionate about it. Geographically, rural and regional areas are closer to a major city and therefore a much higher level of medical/nursing care can be accessed much faster. And in most rural and regional towns there are more health-service providers available, for example doctors, specialists, radiology services and pharmacies which together provide a much greater collegial effort for the patients. 'As a remote midwife, you are almost always the only trained midwife, so you have no one on the ground who is a professional colleague for back-up and assistance, so it's a more autonomous role.

'I also love that autonomy. Clinically you have to be prepared for anything. It's not only having the confidence and competence to work with emergency cases with a minimal amount of equipment and support, but it's also essential to be culturally sensitive. In midwifery terms, Indigenous men have minimal input with a woman's pregnancy. If you have to go to a house to see a woman who's pregnant, there's no way you would mention the word "pregnant" in front of any male member of her family because it's sacred women's business,' Kate says of the communities she has worked with. 'In a lot of communities, you do see men in the health-centre waiting room with their wife or partner, but a lot won't come in to the women's room because they know there are photos on the wall of pregnant women.

'We start talking with the mums early on in their pregnancies about birthing their babies in the hospital and transferring for sit-down,' Kate explains. 'We help them to understand that going to a hospital is the safest option for themselves and their babies. Even for a healthy woman a planned normal delivery can sometimes go awry with tragic consequences.'

Another cultural difference Kate has noticed is that young girls having their first babies are escorted into town by their grandmother or aunt. 'And in my experience it's the grandmothers who name the children, not the parents. If girls go into labour prematurely and the baby is born in the community, then it's the grandmothers who usually come in to support the mothers. It's always a very exciting time with a flurry of activity and celebration for the women and children. While I haven't seen a father come into the health centre at the time of a birth, most are very hands on and involved once the baby is at home.'

Across the Northern Territory, when Aboriginal mothers and babies return to the community, the babies sleep with their mothers, rather than alone in a bassinette or cot, often sharing with older siblings as well. 'That's the way it has been done for thousands of years,' she says. 'The babies are rarely put down – there's always a willing pair of hands to hold or carry them. Babies are almost exclusively breastfed, most for at least two years, anywhere, any time. All babies seem to have many grandmothers and there is certainly no need for a childcare centre.'

In most places there is very strict tribal clan business and customs to abide by. 'Living in a remote community is certainly all encompassing,' Kate says. 'It's Indigenous country and we're here as guests. English is usually a second or third language for most people. Unfortunately, when in conversation or consultation we move constantly between native language and English, so a lot can get lost in translation.'

Once Kate was relieving in a small community in West Arnhem for two weeks as a nurse – not as a midwife. 'I wasn't aware of the antenatal list so it was with surprise when I received a call from a woman just after 1.30 in the morning, to tell me her daughter was having baby pains. *Goodness, where are you?* I asked. With anxiety in her voice the woman replied, *We at the clinic, she can't sit down, she having really bad pains.*' Kate rushed over to the clinic and when she walked in found the young girl was certainly experiencing baby pains. 'She was seventeen and a very small girl,' Kate says. 'She was about seven and a half months pregnant – so a little early. She was at that point of her labour where she felt a desperate urge to go to the toilet. It was difficult to take her obs, but it was important to listen to the baby's heartbeat. I contacted the permanent midwife to come in to assist. There wasn't a doctor in the community.'

Just as the midwife walked in, the young girl's waters broke and almost right away a tiny baby girl with a hearty cry was birthed. 'The baby weighed two-and-a-half pounds [just over a kilogram],' Kate says. 'The time from the call-out to the baby's arrival was less than an hour. Phew! We settled the mother and baby and made sure they were both warm and comfortable. We transferred them both by air to the tertiary hospital later in the morning, where they made great progress.'

Kate's youngest daughter, Sal, says she and her mother are very close. 'I think very highly of my mum,' she says with pride. 'She has always been a tremendous role model for me and my brother and sisters. I have two stepchildren and it's now that I appreciate all Mum did for us,' Sal says. 'Recently I juggled work and a birthday party and my mother-in-law asked how I had managed to do so much when I was working full-time. I thought later, *That's all I know.* Mum always did that. She did it all – it was just a matter of being organised and she passed that skill on to us. I think her mother was the same kind of inspiration for her too.'

In 2012 Kate began flying into an island community in northeast Arnhem to work month on, month off as the permanent midwife. She shares the roster with another midwife. 'It works well for Peter and I,' Kate says. 'When you have someone to share the roster, the job can be very flexible.' On the island the average house occupancy is fourteen to sixteen people in a three-bedroom house. Kate says generally the whole family shares the bedroom and everyone sleeps on mattresses on the floor. 'The people don't have a great deal in the way of material possessions,' she says. 'Respiratory, skin and rheumatic heart disease are a major problem in Indigenous communities. The bush and grass is regularly burnt, which can cause respiratory problems, but largely it's the number of people living in such close quarters that causes infection to spread. Family life tends to be very simple. Power is bought by cards from the store and is supplied by a generator on the island. There's minimal air conditioning, ceiling fans or refrigeration, and in the tropics it can get extremely humid, causing damp clothing and bedding. Aboriginal priorities and perspective of time are often far removed from Western culture. Parents are often unaware of the date of their birthdays or of their children's.'

The health centres operate similarly to a general practice in an urban area, with consultations during office hours, but with a couple of exceptions. 'Firstly there are no appointment times,' Kate says. 'It's first in first served – although as the midwife I do see the maternity women before other patients. Secondly, there's no other health facility or hospital on the island so we have to act as an emergency department as well, day and night. Health staff need to be sensitive to the fact that unlike in urban areas, the local people don't have a choice of health delivery service – we are the only option. All the nurses are rostered "on call" for the after-hours and weekend calls. Up until a few months ago the island only had a locum doctor service, which left the community for weeks without a medical practitioner. We have an emergency room, but there's rarely a doctor on hand after hours. Air evacuations are quite common for the acutely ill requiring 24-hour care or pregnant women in labour.'

For the most part, when Kate's on the island she's on call every second or third night and one day on weekends. The other factor is that as the sole midwife she is on call 24/7 for maternity women. And when she's on call she is on duty on her own most of the time. 'You learn to cope,' she says. 'You just do what you can. If anything goes pear-shaped you can call a colleague.'

In almost all communities the nurses have to drive the ambulance, which is a converted Toyota troop carrier. Having a driver's licence to operate a manual vehicle is essential. 'On the island we are the only permanent emergency service, with the police having to come from a nearby community, which is only possible during daylight hours,' Kate explains. 'Driving on the sand-hill to the houses on the island can take a little bit of getting used to.' Kate's experience driving a four-wheel drive on the farm has stood her in good stead many times in the wet season.

One night in 2011, near the end of the wet season, Kate was in a Victoria River community when a CareFlight plane couldn't land for a patient retrieval due to bad weather. In the two-bed emergency room Kate had a child on the bed with kidney problems, his mother on the floor, another unwell baby sharing the other bed with her fifteen-year-old mother, and her companion escort was on the floor. 'Since the plane wasn't able to land on the wet airstrip at night, we put in an all-nighter. There were no mattresses for the floor, just a blanket – but all my patients and their carers managed to sleep.'

The women in the remote areas Kate works in are the backbone of the communities and provide strong support for each other. 'I've noticed if the women say jump, the men ask how high. Generally they respect the women's decisions and wisdom. There is, however, another side to male and female relationships in remote communities, which I believe stems largely from idleness. Many men are unemployed and so become more controlling of the girls and women. It's very sad to see many teenage girls quite disempowered; they're coerced into a sexual relationship, which often results in a pregnancy. Girls as young as thirteen are having babies. Their bodies haven't matured and emotionally they're not prepared for parenthood. The biological fathers rarely support the girls, often not admitting to paternity. With this situation there comes a whole raft of problems for the families.

'If the baby is a result of non-consensual sex then there is anger and frustration on the part of the girl's family. The grandmothers often know who the father is, but what are their choices? The kinship system is a complex organisational system that determines how people relate to each other and their roles, responsibilities and obligations in relation to one another, ceremonial business and land. The kinship system determines who marries who, ceremonial relationships, funeral roles and behaviour patterns with other kin.'

Today there are increasing numbers of 'wrong skin' marriages, in which people who would traditionally be prevented from marrying become partners. 'The whole kinship arrangement is fractured and when pregnancies occur with the wrong skin it's a difficult situation. The girls themselves are ashamed and don't know how to present to the clinic. Again support is often left to the grandmothers.'

A couple of years ago a woman came to see Kate concerned that her fifteen-year-old daughter was spending her nights out with friends. She was worried about the risk of pregnancy and wanted her daughter to have a contraceptive implant. 'We made several unsuccessful attempts to bring her to the health centre,' Kate says. 'The next time I saw the young girl she came to see me with her grandmother. She tested positively to a pregnancy test and an ultrasound showed the pregnancy was advanced to a stage where even if she had wanted to terminate, it wouldn't have been safe for her. The grandmother more or less took it in her stride, and the girl, who had guessed she was pregnant, took the news calmly.'

A couple of weeks later the girl's mother brought her back to the health centre with her two younger siblings to see Kate. 'I had known the youngest girl since before birth. I presumed the mother had come to talk about the pregnancy, but she didn't offer any information. So when she asked me if her daughter could have the contraceptive implant that day I was completely taken aback. My face spoke a thousand words. She looked at me and said, *She's not is she?* Her daughter was only fifteen – she had to have an escort to travel and the pregnancy had to be reported to authorities. It was indeed a difficult few moments.'

The family left the health centre and the mother returned a few days later, clearly upset. 'She said, *I'm too young to be a grandmother.* She was 32. We had quite a discussion. She felt betrayed that her mother hadn't told her of her daughter's pregnancy. I knew enough background to quietly ask, *Did you tell your mother when you were pregnant at that age?* She hadn't – she had left it to another relative.'

When difficult situations like this arise, there is no reprieve and families understandably have trouble coping. 'The young girl went on to have her baby and relationships were restored – but it did take some time,' Kate says. 'The mother's hope was that her daughter would finish school and go away to study – unlike herself. She had fallen pregnant while away at school in Darwin and had to return home before finishing her education.'

It might be hard to believe that a young girl could mask her pregnancy from her mother for so long, but the women wear long, gathered skirts, often with two or three layers. Two layers hang from the waistline and another over the top hangs from above the bustline with only a T-shirt underneath. So it can be quite difficult to tell if a girl is pregnant.

With one family there was a rather surprising turn of events. Gay was expecting her fourth baby and her pregnancy was complicated by gestational diabetes. Kate found Gay quite difficult to engage with and wasn't sure that she was very happy about being pregnant. 'She didn't want to know about the diabetes,' Kate says. 'She worked at the store, so the prospect of having to regularly travel to the tertiary hospital for monitoring didn't suit her. There didn't seem to be a partner for support, although she had two sisters who were very helpful, and eventually a little boy, Ken, was born.'

Soon after Gay and Ken returned to the community Gay was back at work with Ken left in the care of Gay's two sisters. Ken had a few minor problems and needed admission to the tertiary hospital for growth faltering. As time went by Kate began to wonder if Gay's sister, Mandi, was wet nursing the little boy. Then one morning a local woman rushed into the clinic and said, *Kate – a baby!* 'To my utter surprise, Mandi was brought to the clinic with a baby girl that she had birthed at home. There was quite an anxious period when I had to deliver the placenta with Mandi bleeding quite a lot. But mum and baby were safely transferred by aeromedical evacuation to the tertiary hospital. It was a happily-ever-after story with some wondering how on earth I could miss a woman's pregnancy. But it can be masked well with multiple layers of skirt.'

Travelling to and from a tertiary centre to see an obstetrician can be very difficult for women with problems during their pregnancy – and so it was for Beryl. 'She had a son and daughter who I knew as babies. Over the last couple of years she had lost a baby at eighteen weeks and then twins at 21 weeks, so when she presented to the clinic in early pregnancy we wanted to give her the best possible assistance for a happy outcome. We achieved this but it meant many trips to the tertiary centre for Beryl which was very disruptive for her family life. She endured the ordeal with grace and good humour and, at last, Sylvester was born at 34 weeks gestation and continues to grow beautifully.'

Recently, Kate was surprised and humbled when Beryl presented her with a genuine Yolngu basket, made by her sister. 'Beryl said the children wanted to give me a present – for me, this was a huge honour.'

In Indigenous communities the men hold ceremonies and traditional circumcisions still occur. Boys are initiated into manhood in a cycle of ceremonies where they are taught traditional songs, dances and dreamings. 'They're taken out to the bush where rituals and bush craft are learned, which takes place over many weeks or months,' Kate says. 'The coastal people have quite different cultural beliefs and traditions from the desert people.'

One night Kate was woken by the sound of clapping sticks and corroboree chanting. 'A final ceremony was taking place before the boys would be taken out bush. My phone rang at 4.30 am. Someone had been burnt. I suggested they apply cold water. But the caller said, *No, Yapa [nurse or teacher] really bad burn*. I said, *Okay, I'll come down*.' As part of the ceremony the men had been burning leaves while other men were jumping over them. In the process three men's legs were accidentally burnt. 'When they came in to the health centre I sat two on the floor on towels wet with cold water and put the worst burns victim on the bed. I kept applying cold water and then one after the other, I bandaged them. In mainstream hospitals you don't tend to treat people on the floor. In remote nursing you make the best possible decision for the patient and one of the principles of burns first aid is to apply cold water over a lengthy period as soon as possible – so you get quite inventive.'

Doctors and nurses, locally trained or not, abide by the cultural rules and health-centre protocols. 'With limited resources at the clinics, the Aboriginal health workers are an invaluable resource and provide vital assistance,' Kate says. A program she has been involved with called Strong Women, Strong Baby, Strong Culture has made a difference in communities. Kate works with a community strong woman (a senior woman) in Milingimbi, Judy Lirririnyin, and together they provide the best outcomes for the local women. Judy says she and Kate learn from each other. 'I help Kate with language translation, patient history and cultural ways and she teaches me about Western medication and care. We have a lot fun as we work – and together we work out the best way to care for the patients and expectant mothers.

'The idea is to support the health and wellbeing of pregnant women and children up to three years of age,' she says. 'There's a lot being done now to strengthen family units and cultural practices and to prevent and promote early intervention of lifestyle illness and disease before, during and following pregnancy.' The program recognises the traditional cultural approaches to parenting and lifestyle, supporting pregnant Aboriginal women and their babies through better diet, education and antenatal care. The aim is to increase the birth weight of babies and improve early childhood development.

The program relies on and supports senior women in participating communities in providing direct support to pregnant women and their families. 'The senior women encourage attendance at the health centre for regular antenatal care and provide advice on nutrition,' Kate says. 'The program has a long-term outlook with lasting benefits rather than only treating immediate health problems.'

Kate works in communities steeped in tradition. 'I was consulting with a young pregnant woman who had quite a complex medical condition recently. As we were talking she said, *You know sea turtle?* I said, *Yes I know the sea turtle.*

'*Yes, sea turtle, that my dreaming,* she said. There didn't seem to be a connection between her medical condition and the sea turtle and I worried I may have missed something in the translation. It was clear though, that it was important to her that I knew her dreaming.'

The significance of dreaming came up again for Kate at a later time when a woman she had looked after throughout her pregnancy came to the clinic to see her shortly after she arrived home from hospital with her new baby. 'The baby had a parrot feather entwined into the fringe of her hair. It must have been held with resin of some sort because the feather was well and truly stuck to the hair. I asked if that was her dreaming. *No,* she said, *my dreaming is crow.* I must have looked a little surprised because I hadn't heard of the crow for dreaming. Then to clarify her point she stood up and performed the perfect rendition of a crow mildly flapping its wings and jigging from one leg to the other. We both fell about laughing. Then we discussed the meaning of the feather and she told me it draws the wisdom of ancestors while the baby sleeps. The parrot, she said, was her husband's father's dreaming. Whenever I am taken into cultural confidence like this I think, *What a great thrill and privilege.*'

Family relationships are complex in Aboriginal culture. The social structuring and relationships between people is known as the kinship system. It allows each person to be named in relation to one another. When Aboriginal people accept an outsider into their group they name that person in relation to themselves in order for the person to fit into their society. They like to know in their own minds what the kinship relation of that person is to them and that person must have a defined social position.

A woman with whom Kate had become friendly came to see her at the clinic one day. 'She wrote me a little note asking to adopt me as her sister,' Kate says, smiling. 'My first thoughts were, *I wonder what the culturally appropriate way to respond is?* In another community I had been given an endearing name but not invited into someone's family so profoundly. I thanked her and tried to explain how honoured I felt. The cultural aspect still concerned me so I asked my strong woman friend and teacher (my Yapa) what I should have done. She patiently and kindly explained, *Nothing, you just have to be like a sister and friend.* My Yapa has taught me a great deal about Yolngu culture and she tries valiantly to teach me the language of Yolngu Matha. When I am in the community and hearing the language all around me, I can pick up quite a few words.'

Subsequently, the children and young people of her friend's family and extended family call her Marnyi Bonba (Grandmother Butterfly). 'The name is apt because I do fly in and fly out on a regular basis. The older women of her family call me Bonba. There is quite a complex set of rules for the names people are called inside and outside the family or clan.'

Once on a quiet Sunday morning there was a sudden, torrential downpour in the community Kate was in. 'It was pretty impressive and the gushing water afterwards, likewise. After lunch, I took a walk out the back of my donga [a small transportable building] towards the river with another couple, a nurse and a teacher. We came across a bunch of small boys excitedly catching loads of fish. The fish ranged from three to ten centimetres long and were jumping all over the grass and the road. I raced back to get my camera. When I asked the boys where the fish came from, they chorused, *The sky!* I really thought they were pulling my leg. A man came along with his son and they began to put the fish into an old milk bottle as fast as they could catch them. I asked them the same question – *Where did the fish come from?* The man said, *From the sky after the big rain!* I took his word for it. He told me he had a large dish that he grew fish in then he put them in the river for catching later.'

There is in fact a meteorological explanation for the phenomenon. Scientists say it happens when a waterspout (or tornado) sucks water into a cloud which retains the water until the cloud passes over a warmer ground temperature and it rains. In 2010 it was reported that hundreds of live spangled perch rained down upon the town on two successive days. A tornado was believed to have sucked up the fish, which were then frozen at high altitudes and thawed as they fell – which might have been hundreds of kilometres from the origin. 'Whatever the phenomenon, it was an amazing sight with water rushing and fish flicking over parched ground,' Kate says.

Kate likes to ride a pushbike from her house to the health centre or the shop. At she peddles by, the young women and children call out, *Hey, Marnyi Bonba.* 'Recently Judy, the strong woman with whom I work closely, asked me when I was going on leave and how soon I'd be back. I told her and for me, her response was the ultimate compliment – *Yes, you have to come back and help me with antenates and postnates, you understand Yolngu.'*

CHAPTER

3

Chloe Coker

It was 2 am and Chloe Coker was lying on a mattress in the hallway of a house trying to zone out. She had been sheltering here in the tiny settlement on Milingimbi Island for the past twelve hours. Tropical Cyclone Lam, a massive category-four system, was crossing over and the destructive core was battering the island. Things were getting rough. With roaring wind gusts of up to 260 kilometres per hour, more than 1000 residents were bunkered down in houses. Residents who lived close to the water were in a cyclone shelter – the expected tidal surge was a big concern.

Chloe, in town for a three-month contract as women's health nurse and midwife, was on duty. A born leader, the 30-year-old had done all she could to help the community prepare. She had helped let the locals know what was to happen and suggested they move from their houses if they lived near the water to the cyclone shelter out near the airport. All the houses were cyclone rated, but it was the storm surge that was causing the greatest concern. Cyclone kits and boxes containing basic medical essentials including Panadol, bandages, bandaids, water and heat blankets were prepared for dispatch. 'We made sure our outreach emergency bags were ready in case we didn't have a clinic to return to after the cyclone. We also ensured the house we were bunkering down in was ready – we taped the windows, collected bedding and linen from other houses along with a few other essentials like filling buckets, sinks, washing tubs and baths with water. We knew we would be without water and electricity during and post the cyclone.'

Chloe also made sure high-risk patients had the medication they needed before the cyclone and enough medical supplies for a good period following the cyclone in case access to medication became an issue.

The clinic was near to the water, so everything needed to be off the ground, with power points turned off. Anything essential needed to be on the generator outputs. Now it was just a waiting game. Along with Chloe, there were seven clinic staff in the house. They'd decided to wait it out together. Each person was handling the fear differently. Some were trying to find their own quiet space, others were talking nonstop. A few were quite restless and kept trying to create more protection for the house. Chloe had been talkative at first, but as the storm intensified she'd grown quiet.

In a bid to block out the turmoil she tried to think of other things. Her wedding was just weeks away. She tried to focus on all the jobs that still needed to be done. But falling into a state of meditation was hard work when the house was shaking, tin rooftops were rattling and immense trees were crashing down outside. The noise was horrendous and everyone was terrified.

She couldn't help worrying about the little community. Will everyone be safe? With phone lines cut and the power off, there was no contact with the outside world.

Without warning, water began gushing through the front door and people started to get wet. They sprang into action to push it back out. 'A lady was lying on a mattress a couple of metres from the front door and she told us her mattress had become wet. The water had come into the lounge room and near to the kitchen. It was about an inch deep of water. We used mops, buckets and towels to get the water off the floor. Then we blocked the gap between the front door and the floor with towels. The water was getting in because of the intensity of the rain and the wind.'

It was a long, exhausting night. Finally, at 7 am it was deemed safe to venture outside. Nobody expected the brunt of this cyclone to hit head on.

Meanwhile in Melbourne Chloe's fiancé, Ian Coker, was pacing. Chloe had called a few days earlier to let him know a cyclone was coming. 'She said no one seemed to be taking it seriously and the locals didn't think it would be an issue,' Ian says. 'I thought, *Okay, maybe it's just going to pass nearby and there's nothing to worry about.* But then Chloe called back about 36 hours before it landed and said she was worried. All reports were now saying it's going to land close to Milingimbi.'

Milingimbi Island, 4900 hectares in size, is part of the Crocodile Islands in the Arafura Sea. It's about half a kilometre off the north coast of Central Arnhem Land, 440 kilometres east of Darwin and 200 kilometres west of Nhulunbuy. With a population of more than 1000, predominantly Yolngu people, there are 21 different clan groups. Yolngu people live in locations on the island and the only way to get in is by boat, barge or aircraft.

Up to about eighteen hours before the cyclone hit, only scant preparations were put in place. Chloe still didn't know where she should shelter or what she had to do. The highest point on the island only reaches ten metres, and the storm surge was predicted to be twelve metres high. When Chloe realised things were getting serious, she got behind the late planning efforts and helped get the community sorted.

'She's like that,' Ian says. 'She's all about helping people. She's incredibly calm in a crisis – especially medical emergencies. The police offered to fly her out in the police air wing but she declined. She wanted to stay and help with the clean-up and recovery.'

After the cyclone the town was without power, water and sewerage for several days. Chloe was one of the first out in rescue vehicles to treat injuries, check that people were safe and make sure everyone had adequate water and blankets. Most of the mattresses and bedding throughout the community were soaking wet. Chloe knew all the babies in town and where they lived. 'Earlier some blankets had been donated to the community for the new babies returning from Gove and Darwin hospitals post-birth. Luckily they hadn't been distributed yet and were still dry. So together with the Aboriginal strong women, Judy Lirririnyin and Julie Gapalathana from the health clinic, we got them out to the families with babies and toddlers. Everyone was grateful to have something dry to keep their babies warm. There were some amazing people involved in that recovery.' As community strong women, Judy and Julie work to improve the health of Aboriginal women and their babies. Rather than imposing Western medicine on young women in their community, they encourage traditional cultural practices to strengthen families and improve nutrition and lifestyle. They educate young women about the importance of a healthy diet, and through their support and antenatal care of pregnant women and their babies they help increase babies' birth weights as well as improving early childhood development and health. Milingimbi is a dry community, so there is no alcohol. Many of the health issues community members face stem from Western influence, which has been significantly disruptive to the health of people in these Indigenous communities.

There were also people in the community susceptible to respiratory problems, particularly children with bronchiectasis. Chloe flagged this with the local doctor and wrote a list of names for the recovery coordinator. Bedding was checked and replaced if needed. 'I was paired with Julie and we helped assess the damage and needs for each household. It gave us an opportunity to let people know about the importance of boiling water for drinking, hand hygiene and to deliver crates of bottled water. It also turned out to be a chance for people to debrief about their cyclone experiences.' Chloe had enrolled a couple of months earlier to start her Masters in Public Health degree – she hadn't imagined she'd find herself in a situation so soon where she'd actually need to put public health initiatives to work. 'In general, people spoke about how they sat huddled in the darkness next to their family members and listened to loud and frightening "crash bang" noises. They felt the cold from the rain and wind and their mattresses and bedding were soaked. Many talked about how they prayed that the cyclone would move track. Some experienced large trees falling on their houses or cars and mentioned the fear they felt for the lives of loved ones and of their own. After the cyclone people were concerned about their wet belongings, issues with food, power, lack of running water and the damage to their houses.'

For Chloe the most stressful part was waiting for the cyclone. There had been a lot of reports about it landing close to Milingimbi Island, but the residents were disbelieving. Some years ago a large rock was placed out by one of the islands and locals believed it protected them from cyclones. They had been told before that a cyclone would hit and when it didn't eventuate, they were sure it was all down to that rock. 'There was a lot of denial by everyone on the island,' Chloe says. 'No one believed we'd be hit. Also, because the Bureau of Meteorology [BOM] at one stage showed the cyclone could either come our way or turn to Gapuwiyak, another community in north-eastern Arnhem Land about 25 kilometres south of the head of Buckingham Bay, everyone was complacent and that went on for about a week. I tracked it closely through BOM and by Thursday I realised it was definitely coming our way. The clinic staff had a meeting and we did what we could to prepare.'

When the recovery team flew into Milingimbi, Chloe was relieved to see some familiar faces. As a fly-in-fly-out nurse and midwife Chloe is friendly with most of the police and people working for other agencies in the remote communities she works in. 'It was very nice to see some of those faces from the Darwin Tactile Response Group who came in to help get us back on track. There were myriad jobs to be done. House repairs, adequate drinking water to arrange, sewerage and power to fix and nearly every tree was down. It's very curious how the majority of those trees missed the houses when they fell. With the direction they fell on one side of the street, you'd think the ones on the other side would have fallen the same way and come down on the houses. But they missed them and it didn't make sense. The locals told me they'd been praying and the rock had clearly helped.'

Chloe is the youngest of five children and grew up in Port Macquarie on a farm. Her mother, Pamela, says she was independent and determined from the get-go. 'Because there's quite a gap between Chloe and our eldest child, she became an aunty when she was three years old. We have seventeen grandchildren. She grew up caring for little kids, taking charge and pretty much looking after herself. She's a leader and runs on high energy. With a farm and three shops to manage we were very busy. We'd say, *You right, Chloe?* And she'd say, *Yep, I'm fine.'*

After completing her nursing training through Newcastle University and some tertiary hospitals in Sydney, Chloe, at 23, thought she would give nursing in a remote area a try – just to tick the box. 'I thought I was going out for a one-off experience. I was sent on contract to Port Keats, known as Wadeye, 420 kilometres south-west of Darwin. With a population of 2500 it's one of Australia's largest Aboriginal communities. I was very nervous and a bit naive when I arrived,' she says. 'But I was lucky to work with a bunch of old-school remote-area nurses out there. They took me under their wing and taught me an enormous amount. I worked on call and worked in the clinic from Monday to Friday.' Outgoing and social, Chloe was surprised to find she enjoyed the harshness of a remote community and even the isolation. 'I had to learn how to spend a lot of time by myself and it did take me a little while to adjust. But I soon learned how to fill in my time.'

Initially, Chloe thought a two-month stint would be enough. The nurses she worked with advised her not to go to Central Australia. They said it was very hard going, rough and isolating. But by the end of the two months she'd organised a placement in a community there. 'I worked with the Nganampa Health Council and got to experience the difference for myself,' she says. 'It was a much smaller community and I liked it. Since then I've done quite a lot of locum work in Central Australia and throughout 2010 I juggled contracts between the Nganampa Health Council and Wadeye.'

It was on Chloe's return to Wadeye in 2010 that she birthed her first baby.

'It was on the second night after I'd arrived. I hadn't even met the clinic's midwife yet. The health worker called me in the early hours to say a woman was having baby pains. I didn't know what the process was or who to call. I didn't expect she would be at full term or about to birth. My experience in Central Australia had been that if women experienced baby pains they were signs of a premature labour or a miscarriage – all full-term women were flown out for sit-down. I was very slow to realise I was actually about to assist a woman give birth to a term baby. The woman had been sent out of Wadeye for sit-down but had chosen to return because of family matters.'

Chloe found a woman clearly at full term waiting for her. Her mother was by her side for support. Chloe tried not to look concerned and diligently rang one of the two midwives. 'The first I called lived across the road. She told me I wasn't meant to call her, but to ring the other midwife who oversaw all the midwifery management. The other one lived on the other side of town and she told me she'd brush her teeth, get dressed and come along shortly. She didn't sound happy about coming in so I thought I should do as much as I could. I sent the health worker off to find the women's business manual while I pulled out the IV trolley with the intention of putting a cannula in.' A cannula is a tube that is inserted into the body for the delivery or removal of fluid and intravenous drugs and removal of blood for testing if needed. 'I had a little moment where I thought, *Hmm, something's not quite right*. I looked at the woman and she was calmly watching me and smiling. I thought I'd take a little look and lifted up the sheet. To my surprise a little head was presenting.' Chloe dropped what she was doing and with no time to find gloves she held out her hands just in time to catch a baby boy.

'This young mother was actually smiling at me as she was birthing her baby,' she says. 'I was thrilled and that sense of bewilderment and elation stayed with me for a very long time. The baby pretty much delivered itself within ten minutes of my arrival. And thinking back now, I wasn't a terribly big help. But the experience was defining; that's when I decided to become a midwife.'

Chloe's parents, Pamela and Arthur, visited her in Wadeye a couple of times and watched her work. When Pamela visited in 2010 for a month she was in awe of the effort she saw Chloe put in. 'She'd be on call all hours of the night. One night she left the house at 1 am. She went out bush somewhere because there had been a fight. Someone had sustained a leg injury from a star picket and needed help. When she came back and told me, I was horrified. She just said, *It's fine, Mum. I've done all I can do. I've called the plane and they'll fly him out to Darwin.* That's where I saw her strength.'

At times, there would be physical riots in the streets of town at night and Chloe would be called to go in after the riot had been dispersed to help those injured. Occasionally someone would be flown out for medical treatment, but most of the time injuries could be treated at the clinic. There were two elders in town who looked after Chloe and she would have locals drive her at nighttime. One night following a riot at the airport, Chloe was trying to put a young girl on a CareFlight plane. At one point, she tried to find the drivers but couldn't locate them. After everything settled, the driver team crawled out from under the clinic ute – they had been terrified and were hiding from the rioters. Chloe had been too focused on her job to even consider it.

Chloe took contract work with the Northern Territory government in Wadeye and in different communities for the Nganampa Health Council. 'Wadeye is a very busy place and when I felt I needed a break, I'd go to a smaller community. It would still be busy, but not as stressful.'

When she finished her midwifery training at Deakin University in Melbourne in 2013, Chloe applied for a graduate midwife position at the Mercy Hospital in Heidelberg, Victoria. She knew that to make a good midwife in a remote location she'd need that extra training. With a six-month wait before starting, she took a job at Milingimbi Island to fill in the time. But not as a midwife – she didn't feel ready for that.

When she arrived the staff had heard she'd done her midwifery training. 'When I told them I needed to do my new graduate program in a tertiary setting before I could feel competent to work in a remote setting they said, *We haven't had a midwife for six months – no midwife at all. So we'd prefer to have someone with at least some training rather than a nurse with no mid training*. It took a bit of persuasion because I really wasn't keen to hold that title. But I felt better when they put me in contact with the outreach midwife, Lisa, who turned out to be someone I knew well and was inspired by.'

Prior to Chloe's midwifery training, Lisa was the first person to teach her how to birth a baby in a remote setting. They had worked together in remote communities a few times on the Anangu Pitjantjatjara Yankunytjatjara (APY) lands with Nganampa Health Council. Lisa had taken Chloe through a mock scenario of birthing a baby. 'She showed me where the midwifery packs were kept, oxygen bags and any drugs you might need,' Chloe says. 'I was thrilled that day when I rang the number for the East Arnhem Land outreach midwife, to find it was Lisa. She was incredibly supportive and came out a few times to work with me. We also did a lot of group education together with the girls in Milingimbi, which was really great. I was also able to call on the female doctor based in Darwin any time and she came out a couple of days each month and was incredibly supportive.'

The Milingimbi girls went to Gove for sit-down and had their babies there. The clinic was at that time very small and built right on the edge of the beach. 'It's a very beautiful place,' Chloe says. 'My consulting room was tiny. The shower area had been converted into a storage room and there was a back-door entrance. The girls could knock on the back door if they didn't want to be seen going through the entrance. On my second day in the community the clinic receptionist, Nicki, told me she'd noticed a woman at the shop who looked very pregnant. She didn't know her so assumed she was from another community. She said to me, *You probably should plan to see her on Monday.* It was 4 pm and the clinic closed at five. I thought, *I should try to find her now.* So I sent some health workers off and they brought her in to see me. She was 36 weeks pregnant and visiting from another community. I called the clinic in her usual community and found she'd had minimal antenatal care at her local clinic during this pregnancy. The staff told me she'd spent a fair bit of time in Adelaide because her son was in hospital after a bike accident. She was expecting her fifth child. After an antenatal check I found she had significantly high blood pressure and excessive protein in her urine. She felt well, but those two warning signs had me concerned. I rang the outreach midwife and the Darwin GP to ask advice.

'At that point there were another two emergencies in the clinic and a funeral was going on outside. Earlier that day we were instructed not to put lights on when it got dark because of the funeral. Aboriginal customs and traditions are very different. This was a funeral for a very important community elder and the request was accepted in respect – it's about adhering to cultural need. We used torchlight and medical lamps to create enough light to do our jobs. We thought no worries, nothing much was going on so we could make sure we were back at our houses before dark. But in the end, all of us were held back with the emergencies. When it grew dark we worked in torchlight. Not being able to use the emergency room, I was in the very small back room. I was on my own with a woman and a baby in utero so I was mindful that I was caring for two. As time went on the woman became quite unwell. Her blood pressure rose, her vision blurred and she had a headache and nausea. I administered drugs to manage her blood pressure.'

In that little back room working on her own, Chloe felt nervous. She liaised with the community doctor, who was experienced, but not predominantly in obstetrics. 'We decided to reshuffle our patients because the woman needed more care and evacuation to Darwin. We moved her to a room closer to the emergency room – with someone else still in there.' The doctor and Chloe continued to provide care for the woman with instructions from doctors in Gove, including the ongoing administration of drugs to manage her blood pressure.

The CareFlight plane flew in just as the funeral ended. Perfect timing by coincidence! 'By this stage the woman was very unwell and we quickly boarded her on the plane,' Chloe says. Once in Darwin she was taken straight to theatre for an emergency caesarian and baby Olivia was born. Olivia was very small as a result of pre-eclampsia and intrauterine growth restriction (IUGR), which often go hand in hand, so she stayed in the special-care nursery for a couple of weeks. 'With the mother's four children back on Milingimbi Island with their father, understandably there were some social issues going on with their management. There was involvement from myriad health professionals and ongoing phone calls. But at last, some weeks later, the mum returned to Milingimbi with Olivia and it was time to celebrate.'

Pamela was visiting at the time and with Chloe she was to attend a smoking ceremony for Olivia and another baby. The ceremony is an ancient custom, where various native plants are burnt to produce smoke with cleansing properties and the ability to ward off bad spirits. The ceremony reverses the power of curses and evil spirits. 'We went to a small billabong to watch the babies get smoked,' Chloe says. 'We stopped along the way and the women walked out to an anthill and collected red dirt from the mound. At the ceremony they mixed that with a variety of leaves and sticks and made a very light fire that became smoke only. They smoked the babies and their mothers. The tradition ensures good milk sources and healing powers to make them healthy and strong. The ceremonies are performed for the mothers and babies returning from Darwin to welcome them back to country.'

Pamela says it was a privilege to be there. 'I was moved to think Chloe had picked up on the problem just in time and more than likely had prevented a tragedy. She saved their lives. It was her first real experience of remote midwifery and I was immensely proud of her. She clearly had a connection with the women and loved spending as much time as she could with them. They were at case with her and vice versa.'

On her days off in numerous communities Chloe worked in, she often joined the locals to hunt for crabs in the mangroves and mud. 'I also made good friends with Ramingining police officers, who often invited me to go fishing with them. There was occasionally an odd crocodile spotting, which was always exciting.' The locals warmed to Chloe and regularly invited her to travel out to their homelands. Back in Wadeye she'd set out in her Jeep Wrangler packed to the rafters with Aboriginal friends and off they'd go. 'We'd hunt all day, mainly for fish and crabs, and then sit around a camp fire eating together and sharing stories. I learned how to make damper Indigenous style by one of the best damper makers in Wadeye and I learned about bush tucker.

'During my time at Milingimbi there were usually around twelve to fifteen girls pregnant at any one time. The pregnancies are generally very complex with a lot of cases of anaemia and gestational diabetes,' Chloe says. 'Managing these takes quite a lot of work. The girls are all beautiful and it's very special when you get to know them during their antenatal care. Being there for them during their pregnancy and again when they return with their babies from whatever hospital they went to for their sit-down and birthing is wonderful.'

One night Chloe was to be on call at Milingimbi Island when a woman at 32 weeks pregnant was brought into the clinic by the permanent midwife and Aboriginal health worker. It was 4 pm. The midwife requested Chloe to provide care and initiate the CareFlight retrieval of the woman, who was at that point in threatened premature labour. Sylvie, a medical student, was visiting Milingimbi for remote experience and was working alongside Chloe. Chloe was grateful to have Sylvie at her side to assist. 'I was asking for things unfamiliar to her. I had to quickly get across what I needed – I was teaching as well as trying to birth a baby. The room wasn't set up for a delivery and we needed things – like obstetric gear, a delivery pack, baby items, oxygen, a paediatric flow metre, warming gear, towels – it all needed to be brought in from other areas of the clinic. We needed to turn the room into a birthing room and be ready to go.'

Chloe knew the baby would be born soon and worst-case scenarios were going through her head. 'I thought, *Please don't let this baby come out screaming – that might only be the response to the baby's natural adrenaline and that's not what we want. It will be good at first, but when the adrenaline runs out the baby's drive will drop.*'

Twenty minutes after the woman's arrival, the baby birthed with no time for the steroids and antibiotics injected into the mother to take adequate effect for the baby in utero. The baby was slow to respond at first, but didn't need any major resuscitation. 'It was slowly pinking up and took its first whimper, then a cry,' Chloe says. 'And there were no respiratory issues. The Apgar score [a newborn's first test] wasn't bad – initially seven out of ten and then hovering around seven to eight. The baby slowly grew more alert and cried louder. It needed a little oxygen support, but really it was fine. It weighed nearly two kilograms – a really good size for a 32-weeker.

'Sylvie loved it – it was her first experience of seeing a birth. We have kept in touch and she still talks about how great that experience was.' Chloe and Sylvie waited more than three hours for the CareFlight team – a flight nurse and paediatrician – to arrive and the baby and mum were flown to Darwin.

During her time in remote communities Chloe has seen a lot of miscarriages. Once on Groote Eylandt she responded to an after-hours call-out for a woman with a threatened miscarriage. Her husband had brought her to the clinic. She already had two children and this was an unplanned pregnancy. 'She had only just found out she was pregnant a few days prior and hadn't told many people,' Chloe says. 'And because she hadn't had an ultrasound as yet, we didn't know if it would be a straightforward miscarriage or an ectopic pregnancy. There was significant bleeding and she was in a lot of pain. She wasn't in a critical state or leaning towards an ectopic pregnancy, so after discussion with the rural medical practitioner on call, I was happy to manage her in the community overnight.'

The woman made it clear to Chloe she didn't want to be pregnant. It's not uncommon for midwives to find themselves involved in discussions about unplanned and unwanted pregnancies. 'The law around terminations differs between states and territories,' Chloe says. 'The Northern Territory has the lowest period of weeks where women can legally have terminations. Sometimes if a woman wants one she may need to be sent interstate for the procedure at her own expense. There's a lot of prejudice and debate about it and the topic arises frequently in the Territory. Currently, there are talks about introducing a medical termination of pregnancy [using a drug – a practise already used in other Australian states] instead of surgical. It's a topic of controversy and an issue I've found difficult as a midwife working in remote areas. We need to be non-judgemental and try to provide the woman with an equitable service. Women in the bush should have the same reproductive rights and access as those in the city.

'The next day, after an ultrasound, it was found that despite the blood loss overnight, the woman had a viable pregnancy. She didn't miscarry. But she still didn't want to be pregnant. She was too advanced to have a legal abortion in the Northern Territory so she planned to travel with her husband to Perth. I assisted in organising her journey and supported her. I put her in touch with the right contacts and processes. I'm not sure of her outcome, because my contract ended and I flew out the next day.'

Once in Central Australia Chloe was heading to the clinic in a troopy (a troop carrier) when a woman waved at her to stop. 'She told me her daughter had something wrong with her boob. I didn't know her daughter had had a baby. She was in her early twenties and as she walked towards me I could see one breast was significantly larger than the other. She had serious mastitis and it was the first time I'd seen it in an Aboriginal woman. Generally magnificent breastfeeders, the women tend to feed all the time so they rarely suffer from blocked ducts. But this girl was in great discomfort and it took quite a long time to relieve her pain. She couldn't let her baby feed on one side, she needed antibiotics and to have her breast drained. I spent a lot of time in the clinic that weekend with her and kept in touch by phone consultation with an excellent female doctor for ongoing advice. I was able to get the baby back on the breast some hours after her initial presentation. We continued her on a course of intravenous and then oral antibiotics and it took nearly a week for the mastitis to completely resolve.'

At the Aboriginal community of Bidyadanga, 190 kilometres south of Broome in Western Australia's Kimberley region, Chloe was contracted for a two-week stint over the Easter period. As she was now engaged to Ian, she was no longer working full time in remote areas, but she continued to fly back and forth as often as she could to wherever she was needed. Early in the morning on Easter Monday Chloe heard children singing out her name from outside her house. She smiled and grabbed her things. The day before the Aboriginal Liaison Officer at the health clinic, Barb, had invited Chloe to spend the day with her family. Knowing the visiting nurse/midwife in town would be at a bit of a loose end on the public holiday, Barb had asked Chloe if she had any plans. 'Whenever I was called out, day or night, I would go to Barb's house to collect her in the clinic ambulance and together we would go to the clinic and sometimes a house to see a patient,' Chloe says. 'Barb often brought along her grandchildren – "grannies". I was on call the whole week and I got to know and really enjoy the time with Barb and her grannies.'

Set to go, she raced out to Barb's grannies and waited out front with them to be picked up. Within minutes a ute flowing over with Barb's family came clanking down the road and pulled up. 'We all piled in and drove for nearly two hours,' says Chloe. 'I was absolutely in awe when we arrived at the most spectacular place I have ever seen. We were on the banks of a crystal-clear river, lined with sprawling trees. The river spilled into the ocean. We swam and fished and laughed most of the day. Then we piled back into the ute for an hour to meet up with other Aboriginal families who had also been out hunting and fishing. We came together and cooked our catches. One family had caught a large turtle and gave it to Barb's family. When we got back to Bidyadanga Barb's son-in-law showed me how he extracts the turtle meat and cleans the shell. They told me they would cook the meat and then dry the shell and paint on it.'

Chloe was aware she had experienced a very special day. She had been given an opportunity very few people come by. 'I kept telling myself how amazing it was and how lucky I was to be sharing something so unique.' She stayed in the community until the end of that week and when she left she was driven out on the community mini-bus back to Broome to return home to Melbourne. She drove through town and when they passed Barb's house her heart sank. 'I thought I would've had the chance to say goodbye to Barb at the clinic that morning, but she didn't turn up.' Not far along the road the driver called out to Chloe. 'Hey I think they want you,' and pointed to the back of the bus. Through the back window Chloe could see Barb and her big bunch of grannies chasing the bus along the road, waving hands and yelling out. The driver pulled up and flung open the door. The grannies scampered up and ran to Chloe, smothering her in cuddles. She hopped off the bus, holding back tears, and fell into Barb's arms to hug her. 'I thanked her for having me in her community and for giving me one of the most unforgettable times of my life.'

Based back in Melbourne, Chloe signed up for her Masters in Public Health, and apart from an intensive block of study in Darwin, she studied at home. 'I had completed the basic level of the Major Incident Medical Management and Support (MIMMS) course in 2009 and after Cyclone Lam I decided to complete the advanced commander course of the MIMMS, which I completed early last year in Darwin. The course is designed as a preparation to manage an overabundance of patients or victims in a mass casualty, such as a cyclone, earthquake, train derailment or terrorist attack.'

On top of this, Chloe had a mid-semester wedding to plan. Two weeks after she and Ian were married she flew back to a community in Central Australia and later to the Tiwi Islands, Groote Eylandt and Maningrida a few times. Chloe was well known by the Northern Territory government. They knew she could fly into a community and hit the ground running wherever she was needed. She could stay out for as little as four nights and anywhere up to three months. 'It was great because it fitted in with their schedule and my university work.'

In 2015 Chloe and Ian planned to move to Darwin. But not long before they were due to leave, Ian's company needed him in Adelaide. 'We were both a bit disappointed at first,' Chloe says. 'But within two weeks of being here I got a job with the Royal Flying Doctor Service [RFDS] and we're both really enjoying South Australia. I had aspired to a career with the RFDS for a long time and had been working towards it since graduating as a nurse.' All RFDS flight nurses require

their midwifery certification as they transfer pregnant, labouring and postnatal women who may require a higher level of
obstetric care than is available in their town or community. As
a flight nurse, Chloe now flies across country South Australia
and sometimes interstate to transfer people to tertiary hospitals. She hopes to do some relief work in the Alice Springs and
Port Augusta RFDS bases in the future. 'I'm working in remote
Aboriginal communities – which is what I love most.'

4

Marg McDonald-Ashe

A cluster of small children squealed with delight as the four-wheel drive pulled up in front of the Ingomar Station homestead. They had been waiting for days for the Remote and Isolated Children's Exercise (RICE) team to arrive. When the back doors flung open and the kids saw that the vehicle was packed to the gills with toys and games, their squeals became heightened. They eagerly helped unpack, and in no time, they were deeply absorbed in this highly anticipated day of serious play.

There isn't a 'Welcome to the outback' sign anywhere in Australia, but you know you've passed through the gateway when not far into the journey across sparsely settled country the earth begins to redden and the landscape becomes a panning shot of harshly coloured, sweeping plains. Nurse and midwife Marg McDonald-Ashe and her RICE colleagues, Manoah

McRae and Nicole Yendall, arrived from their base in Port Augusta to run a play day and health checks for the Ward family and some neighbouring families who had also come into Ingomar.

Marg, now 58, is a mobile family health nurse and midwife and she travels out to far-flung places in remote South Australia to provide child health care and antenatal and postnatal care for women living on stations. Marg visits these remote families to do universal health checks for newborn babies and maternal health checks for their mums which might include C-section wounds, mastitis or breastfeeding problems. She liaises with the Royal Flying Doctor Service (RFDS), particularly when she finds women with infections or suffering from postnatal depression. Sometimes she travels with a RICE team, sometimes she goes alone. 'Mothers and children will travel up to four hours to attend a playgroup and health check,' she says. 'If they're meeting at a community centre, they turn up early to clean the place for everyone and they bring copious amounts of food to share whether they're meeting in a community or at a station.'

When the RICE four-wheel drive pulls in, it's like Christmas for the kids. 'They get so excited when they see the toys,' Rinnah Ward, a mum under Marg's care, says. 'The RICE team sets up loads of activities and if it's hot they include lots of water play. They bring fresh fruit out for us and we all sit down for morning tea and lunch together. Everyone brings a plate to share. The mums yarn while the RICE team keeps the kids amused. Marg is a wonderful storyteller and interacts beautifully with the kids.'

With several complications during Rinnah's pregnancy, Marg was one of the midwives who supported her and she continues to do so with postnatal and child health care. 'There's nothing Marg hasn't been able to help me with,' Rinnah says. 'She's the best person you could ever find for the job – she's very experienced and is really, really good at what she does.'

Rinnah's baby suffers from food intolerance and from a very young age she was incredibly irritable. 'Marg is our first point of contact, so I called her for advice,' Rinnah says. 'She was so supportive and recommended a specialist. We had a difficult time and Marg really helped us through it. Having her come to us is amazing and we can call her on the phone any time. It's a long way for us to go anywhere for medical support, and difficult with little children. Marg comes to us regularly and takes the time to sit down with us to chat and discuss any issues we have.'

Marg is away from home on average two nights a week and stays overnight on the cattle stations or small towns she visits. Her destination and time away are determined by the dates babies are born and where they live. In some cases, women living in isolated areas and in extreme conditions cope exceptionally well. 'My hat goes off to those women. They just take it all in their stride and are very resilient and incredibly positive. Others, who are perhaps newer to the bush, can find the isolation difficult. In a lot of cases women marry a cattleman and suddenly find they're living in the bush without access to resources, and in particular, close family. This can cause quite a high level of postnatal depression, which can be a given in remote areas – and that's why we're here.'

A non-government organisation initiated 40 years ago to assist people living along the railway line and on cattle stations in remote South Australia, RICE is administered by the people it services. The vast job environment was quite a change for Marg, who had previously worked in country hospitals and health clinics based in remote Aboriginal communities. Her workplace spans 655,000 square kilometres from the mid-north to northern South Australia up to the Queensland border. Each year Marg travels more than 40,000 kilometres to deliver health care. She takes her nursing and midwifery skills to parents on stations with newborns through to five-year-olds, and does antenatal and postnatal checks for mothers. 'We provide in-home health care as well as "on-air" sessions for children and parents and we keep people up to date with the latest and greatest.'

Some of the places Marg visits include Mannahill, Broken Hill, Birdsville, Oodnadatta, Marree and the Flinders Ranges – calling into cattle stations along the way. She regularly travels the iconic Strzelecki Track and Birdsville Track across desert country and along the edge of the vast Lake Eyre basin. The 459-kilometre Strzelecki Track was pioneered by bushman Harry Redford in 1871 and is only passable to conventional vehicles during the dry season. Pull up on the side of the road and you begin to understand the sense of emptiness and desolation explorers must have felt 150 years ago as they struggled over parched, stony, red earth. If Marg is travelling with others they spend time planning and organising other trips, email and make phone calls until they have driven out of range. 'If I'm travelling alone, I listen to podcasts audio books, Radio National or music,' she adds. 'I do get sick of driving sometimes and I have to do a lot of walking plus long bone and lower back exercises to counteract the long sitting – but generally I love my bush car office.'

Recently, the RICE team travelled to Oodnadatta for a health expo run by the town's health clinic at the local gym. After recent rain the stony plains and rocky hills were covered in wildflowers, and stands of glistening red river gums and coolabah trees lined the waterways.

With the four-wheel drive packed with scales, the mobile toy set-up, hearing- and vision-testing equipment, measuring and weighing gear for observational developmental check-ups to make sure the babies are meeting the milestones, Marg rolled into town with

Nicole, the crèche/play day leader, and Manoah, the wellbeing and social worker. Oodnadatta has a roadhouse, a school, a health clinic and a pub that was on the Ghan train line. But there haven't been any trains through here for more than 30 years. Today it's a largely Aboriginal community with limited services.

With the aquatic play set up, the kids washed dolls and cars, floated boats and sprayed coloured paint on cloth. It was organised chaos, and each child lapped up the rare opportunity for group play. 'It's lovely to watch the transition from shy bush kids to noisy, active participants as the day moves on,' Marg says.

Marg takes a mobile story puppet show with her to stations and events. 'The puppet show and storytelling are a fun and effective way to help children with speech delay. And they're more relaxed when we go on to do a health check because they're not in a clinical environment. In the bush child speech delay is not uncommon – but with some help this can be turned around.'

In between the water play, Marg provides antenatal information for pregnant mothers and discusses all things maternal, including where to birth the babies. Mothers make the most of the chance to talk over any concerns, ask questions and share stories. Marg also fits in the preschooler and six-month child checks. 'I make sure the hospitals let me know, particularly if it's across the border in Queensland, when the babies are born so I can arrange to get back to the families once they're home for their postnatal visits.'

Marg's bush experience goes back to her bush nursing days in remote Aboriginal communities. 'Back then there was very little support out in the field,' says Paul, Marg's husband. 'She was pretty much the sole operator in remote places. It was very much pioneering work and she had to be self-reliant. When you're out there you experience droughts and floods and all the extreme conditions that come with living in remote areas.

She learned how to keep an eye on the weather, road conditions and vehicles – she was a quick learner when it came to bush skills and she's not a quitter. She's only five-foot-three and small-framed, but she can change a tyre on a four-wheel drive and will be the first to get in and get the work done. Her current job has brought together all the skills she's accumulated over the years in midwifery, nursing, teaching and remote settings. You'd be hard-pressed to find somebody with the experience and skill sets like Marg's and who can work on any front.'

Marg has the ability to deal with anything that comes along and she has great empathy for the people living in remote places. 'I've been out with her and I've seen how much station people appreciate what she does,' Paul says. 'They know how far she travels and how much she cares – you can see the appreciation and joy on their faces when she turns up.'

On a recent trip to a station near Broken Hill to visit two families with young children, Marg finished at one house and as she arrived at the second family's house the husband called in on the two-way radio. He just said, 'Tell Marg, go now, go now!' Torrential rain had come unexpectedly and fast. The usual one-and-a-half hour drive took Mark nearly two and a quarter hours with slipping and sliding through the rain and mud. 'It was actually a pretty hairy drive,' Marg says. 'I arrived back with a vehicle covered in mud – not a speck of white to be seen.' Days like that can be long and trying.

The RICE team often drives to the lead- and zinc-mining town, Roxby Downs, 570 kilometres north-west of Adelaide, where they stay the night before heading out the next morning to Stuart Creek Station, 40 kilometres north of Roxby Downs and bordered by Lake Eyre South. The short-lived watercourse Stuart Creek runs through the property's sandhills, breakaways, mound springs and gibber plains. 'Recently with our health checks, playtime and postnatal visit done, Manoah and I continued along the Oodnadatta Track to overnight at the pub. This put us closer to Marree, our next day's destination.' In Marree's town centre beside the old railway line is outback legend Tom Kruse's timeworn mail truck that he drove on the track between Marree and Birdsville delivering mail from 1936 to 1957. Rolling stock stands rusting at the disused station. It's a true desert settlement and the town's solitude and isolation is palpable.

The following morning Marg and Manoah drove along the Birdsville Track, past Lake Harry Station, Clayton Station and on to Dulkaninna Station for more postnatal and new-baby checks. Marg tries to visit mothers and new babies within the first month of a birth for the 'universal' contact visit.

After Dulkaninna they went on to stay the night at the Birdsville Hotel. The next morning they backtracked 30 minutes south-west of Birdsville to Pandi Pandi Station for a six-month-old baby and four-year-old check-up. Then they travelled back down to Marree for the night before returning to Port Augusta the next day. The drive from Birdsville to Port Augusta is 896 kilometres and takes nearly fifteen hours.

The RICE days provide just as much fun and benefit to the mothers as they do for the kids. 'When you're worried about your child, it helps to swap notes with other mothers and share experiences,' Marg says. 'We also run a mother's group tele-conference which is very popular. It's a phone link-up, where expectant mothers and mothers with babies and young children can exchange information, support one another and discuss child development and health. Sometimes we bring a child expert in to talk on a subject.'

Born in 1957, Marg grew up in Sydney's Sutherland Shire and was one of five children. With a hankering to become a

nurse, she completed her training with an emphasis on paediatrics in 1978. After some time travelling extensively overseas with a friend, she returned to Australia to work in several
nursing positions. In 1988 she trained as a midwife at the Lyell
McEwin Hospital in Adelaide, and while she was there a friend
who had worked as a bush nurse in a remote area suggested
Marg give remote nursing a go.

Marg found placements in remote Aboriginal communities
in South Australia as a locum, and while she waited for a permanent position she updated her accident and emergency skills
at the Alice Springs Hospital.

In 1989 she began as nurse and midwife for Urapuntja Health
Services in Central Australia's Utopia region, 350 kilometres
north-east of Alice Springs. Urapuntja consisted of thirteen
outstations (homeland centres) located on the eastern perim-
eter of the Western Desert and covering more than 6000 square
kilometres. Marg was based at Urapuntja with one other nurse.
They took turns to have every third weekend off and generally
drove the three hours to Alice Springs for a break. 'At the time
a lot of our work was over the two-way radio and we liaised
with the RFDS. Aboriginal Health workers were based at several of the outstation communities and we talked to them every
morning. They relayed medical cases or emergencies and let us
know if anyone was unwell. We regularly drove out to the outstations in a vehicle fitted out like a mobile clinic.'

The accommodation on outstations was less than basic. 'At
Munindunginya our lodging was a small tin shed,' Marg says,
laughing. 'We had to light a donkey heater [a fire lit in a barrel]
to get hot water and we had an emergency generator that we
had to crank to start.'

Three weeks after Marg's arrival in Urapuntja a heavily
pregnant woman with baby pains presented at the clinic door

after dark one night. 'I heard cars and people arriving, so I went out to see what was happening,' she recalls. 'The woman was lying on the ground and I had to examine her right there and then outside the clinic using torchlight.' With some help, Marg moved the woman into the clinic. 'We managed to get her in and settled and I prepared for the birth,' Marg says. 'I was still in my late twenties and new to midwifery. Knowing a neonatal medical team was a long way away, I was frightened. I could see the baby was about to arrive and knew the RFDS wouldn't get there on time,' she says. 'More women arrived and sat outside the clinic and sang through the night to support the expectant mum.'

To Marg's great relief the baby birthed a few hours later in the early hours of the morning. There were no complications, and the mother and child returned a few days later to their outstation. 'I visited every day to check on them both,' Marg says. 'And I was thrilled to be invited to attend the baby's smoking ceremony held one morning at dawn. I arrived to find the baby asleep next to her mother in a little indented coolamon [a traditional Indigenous carrying vessel carved from wood] lined with batik. It was very poignant.' The women in the Urapuntja region are very well known for their extraordinary art and batik work.

Six months later another woman with labour pains presented at the clinic. 'She was in second-stage labour and already ten centimetres dilated,' Marg says. 'She wasn't far off birthing, and expecting her sixth child, I knew she was at risk of a postpartum haemorrhage (PPH). I rang the RFDS and spoke to a new doctor. He was Scottish and I had trouble understanding his accent over the crackly radio. He was trying to tell me to bring her in – but there wasn't time and as I couldn't hear or understand what he was saying, I switched the radio off.

I thought, *I just have to focus on this birth that's about to happen and just do all I can to help.* The birth was uncomplicated and my colleague, who was better at suturing than me, gave the mother some necessary stiches. Later I ended up working with the woman whose baby I helped birth. She was a health worker and we became great friends as a result of that unexpected but wonderful birth.

'We visited the mum and baby every day for five days across the Sandover River,' Marg says. 'Unfortunately, after that big rain fell and the river came up. We watched as the water rose quickly and knew we wouldn't be able to get back over for quite some time.'

After twelve months on the job at Urapuntja Marg fell very ill with infected gallstones and needed surgery. She flew to Sydney for an operation and with complications was hospitalised for six weeks, and it took her quite some time to return to the Territory. 'I wasn't able to go back to full-time work until 1992 – nearly two years after falling ill,' Marg says. 'I started work for the Central Australian Aboriginal Congress as an Aboriginal health educator. It involved teaching health workers in Alice Springs and out in communities.'

In her late thirties, Marg met Paul. He'd been working in Aboriginal health and education for a long time and had two children, Anthony and Katherine, from a previous marriage. They met when they were both in the Northern Territory for the second time around.

Wanting a break from nursing, Marg had been in Sydney to train as a teacher in the Steiner education system. 'I applied for a job in Katherine and Marg was encouraged to apply for the founding teacher's job at a new Steiner school in Alice Springs,' Paul says. 'We both got the jobs and we were there at the same time when a mutual friend asked if I'd like to take a passenger with me on my upcoming drive to Sydney. Marg wanted to visit her sister in northern New South Wales for Christmas. I thought, *Well, you don't want to go on a long trip like that with someone you don't get along with, we should meet first.'*

So the two met and within days were off on the long road trip to New South Wales. Along the way they camped and got to know each other well. 'It was a really nice road trip and I dropped Marg off at her sister's place,' Paul says. Back in the Territory they met up again close to Easter time and began a relationship

Paul and Marg married in 1997, a year after meeting. Their daughter, Leah, was born in 1998 when Marg was 40, and Jack came along in 2000 when she was 42. 'They were born at the Alice Springs Hospital and I had a midwife,' Marg says. 'The hospital had a very innovative midwifery clinic and I didn't have to see a doctor – even though I was considered high risk having a baby in my forties. Because of my slight build, medical staff insisted my daughter was too small. But Paul's only five-foot-three as well and I knew everything would be fine. I went on to have a normal, natural birth and midwives visited me for postnatal care. We did consider a homebirth when I was pregnant with Leah, but because Anthony, who I call my bonus son, was seventeen and staying with us when she was born, I didn't think he'd want to see that.' When the kids were little Marg juggled a few casual jobs, including a position with the health department as a community nurse on weekends and as a midwife at the Alice Springs Hospital. She'd race home and breastfeed on her breaks.

As Paul is originally from Yorkshire in England, he and Marg decided to spend some time in England when Leah and Jack were four and two years old. 'Paul was recovering from hip surgery, so he stayed at home to mind the children while

I worked full-time as a midwife at the Southmead Hospital in Bristol,' Marg says.

Working in a large hospital, Marg assisted births every day. 'I did an upskilling course there and was required to attend 100 births in sixteen weeks. I was a busy girl. In Australia at the time, training midwives only had to attend twenty normal and twenty abnormal births. At Southmead there were 5000 births a year and with a wonderful training and mentor system at the hospital I learned a great deal.' After that Marg worked with the hospital's home midwifery team. She lived 45 minutes from Bristol in a rural community and later she got work with a nursing service that ran a team of six midwives to assist families in rural villages.

'We worked twelve-hour days on either day or night duty. The work also involved antenatal, birthing and postnatal care for female prisoners. In England, women can choose to have a hospital birth or a homebirth and the National Health System supports both. I would follow through with the woman in my care and one of us would be there for the birth, and a second midwife was always in attendance. The system for homebirths is extremely well set up in the United Kingdom. I did this for twelve months and loved the diversity. One day I could be caring for a mum struggling in a very poor district and the next I could be with a wealthy family living in a beautiful historic home on farmland. Paul and I had an old Sherpa van decked out with hammocks and we tripped all over the place on weekends and holidays. It was a wonderful family time.'

After their period in the UK the family returned to Australia and moved to the Eyre Peninsula in South Australia to be near Paul's family. Marg worked as a nurse and midwife at Cleve District Hospital in the rural heart of the Peninsula. 'It was a small twenty-bed facility and the doctor was usually around, but only came in for a birth if there was a complication,' Marg says. 'I was honoured to be at the last birth in that small country hospital before the facility had to fold and women had to have their babies in a larger area.'

In 2007 with a new adventure high on the agenda, Marg and Paul took the children to Canada, where Marg worked as a nurse and midwife for twenty months. 'I had to sit a nursing exam in Canada first, so Paul and I flew over and my sister looked after the kids for ten days,' Marg says. 'We'd met some Canadians by chance on a road trip in South Australia and they suggested we think about Terrace, where they lived. When we decided to go, we made contact with a hospital in Terrace, where one of their relatives worked. I passed the exam and got the job and was given a relocation allowance, which paid for our move. Lea was nine and Jack was seven.'

Terrace is four hours from the Alaskan Panhandle in southeast Alaska, northern British Columbia. It was a logging town with a population of 20,000, including an Indigenous population of about 3000. 'There was a river through the middle of the town and we found it very similar to Alice Springs – just in the northern hemisphere,' Paul says. 'It was surrounded by remote communities and we got to know quite a lot of the Indigenous people in town.' At the hospital where Marg worked, the midwives cared for pregnant women right up to the last minute before the birth and then the doctor would usually come in.

One day Marg was caring for a baby who was very slow at feeding and hadn't picked up. 'The baby was tired after feeding,' Marg says. 'We called in a paediatrician to take a look and it was found the baby had a heart condition and needed to be flown out. The plane couldn't come in for three days due to bad weather, so I cared for baby until it could land. The father of the baby was the local dentist. I went to him a few months later and he talked me into some expensive dental work. I went ahead with it reluctantly, and then he wouldn't charge me.'

Marg loved working in Terrace. 'As Paul wasn't eligible for a work visa he did the parenting and some volunteer migrant literacy and numeracy teaching. All our married lives we've swapped the breadwinning job – sometimes I'm the principal earner and sometimes Paul is. It's worked really well for us.'

While in Canada the family toured a lot of the country and at one stage the health services department called for nurses to do some work on Queen Charlotte Islands (now known as Haida Gwaii), an archipelago off British Columbia's northern coast. 'On my days off I flew in by seaplane for two lots of four days. The pilots knew I was an Aussie tourist and flew low so I could get a really good look. Made up of more than 200 mostly uninhabited islands, Haida Gwaii is home to an abundance of sea life and onshore, seabird colonies, bald eagles and bears. It's a spectacular place,' Marg says. 'We have had so many rich travel experiences through my midwifery work. Leah and Jack absolutely loved the school in Terrace and were very happy there. Jack didn't want to leave. Katherine and Anthony visited and Anthony stayed with us for eighteen months.'

A new position came up at the Cleve Hospital in 2008, so Marg applied for it while she was still in Canada and got the job, so the family moved back to South Australia. 'I worked as a general nurse and did some midwifery community work. Paul worked in Port Lincoln and commuted from Cleve. In 2011 we decided to move to the little town of Willowie, a farming community in the Flinders Ranges, 65 kilometres southeast of Port Augusta. It has a population of 30 and there are no shops. But we're only twenty minutes from several larger country towns. We still live in Willowie and we all love it here.

The children are now at school in Port Pirie to give them more subject options and extend their social life – a common reality of remote and rural life.'

When the maternity ward closed at Cleve, Marg began work with the Crystal Brook midwifery clinic team, 197 kilometres north of Adelaide. It was similar to the rural midwifery work she did in England, and she enjoyed working there for more than eighteen months. Her friend and colleague Liz Morris-Elliott worked with Marg at Crystal Brook. 'Nothing was ever too much trouble for Marg, she'd go out of her way to help, even when she lived so far out of town. She showed initiative and was incredibly dedicated. We worked across both the Port Pirie Regional Health Service and Crystal Brook Hospital sites and had our midwifery caseloads. We worked very much in a team. On one occasion I'd worked a really long day, pushing fifteen hours and Marg came in to relieve me in Port Pirie,' Liz says. 'I was caring for a young woman with pre-eclampsia and she was in established labour. I couldn't stay on with her, because I was very tired and well over my twelve-hour limit. While I was handing over to Marg and sitting at a desk writing notes so Marg would know where everything she might need was, the woman had a seizure. Marg and I flew into action together. Afterwards I said to Marg, *Wow, I'm so glad it was you that was here with me.* We just worked really well together in that emergency situation. And it was nice to know someone with her experience and expertise was there to support me.'

The hospital was small at Crystal Brook, with quite rustic conditions compared to the bigger regional hospitals. 'We had to make do and Marg's remote-nursing experience was a great help – she was always coming up with innovative solutions and she took everything in her stride,' Liz says. 'Marg doesn't shy away from hard work and she continues to give and give and give.'

Marg took a break from on-call work, and family wise she was happy, but before too long she started to miss midwifery, which led to her current work as nurse and midwife with RICE.

In October 2015 Marg received the Health Award from the South Australian Regional Awards – from more than 2000 nominations across seven regions. She was recognised for her unique and challenging role providing a broad variety of health services to geographically isolated families across the vast pastoral and outback areas of South Australia. She was also recognised for re-establishing the phone link-ups for pregnant women and women with young children to enable them to exchange information. She accepted her award at a ceremony in Port Augusta. When RICE management called Marg into the office to let her know she'd won, she didn't think for a minute it would be about an award. 'I thought I was going to get in trouble for the aerial that had fallen off my vehicle – which I hadn't reported,' she says, laughing.

Marg's award meant a lot to her family, particularly Paul, because it was an acknowledgement of the pioneering work people still do in the bush. 'They stretch themselves in all sorts of ways to deliver services with limited resources. Marg is out there doing the hard yards – I've been out with her and you could tell how much the people she sees appreciate her. They know how far she travels to help them, and at times in pretty awful conditions. She makes a big difference to the lives of many people.'

CHAPTER

5

Mark Holmes

Mark Holmes' first day on the job working as a midwife in a major hospital began on a high. Brimming with cheerful anticipation, the 23-year-old entered the birth suite to meet the young woman who had been assigned to his care. Conscious of the importance of building a positive relationship with the expectant mother and her family, he was keen to gain their trust and confidence. He wanted them to feel completely at ease with their midwife.

A bottle of champagne sat on a bench in the room, ready to pop on the baby's arrival. In the excitement of the pending birth with the parents, Mark chatted happily about his liking for a bit of champagne. Warming to their six-foot-one, broad-framed midwife, the young couple enjoyed sharing stories and jokes with Mark. They appreciated the talking and laughing. It eased the nervous wait.

Everything was going swimmingly – until the woman's second stage of labour when the best of his midwifery skills were unexpectedly called on. Out of the blue he had to perform his first ever episiotomy – a surgical incision to quickly enlarge the opening for the baby to pass through. It was the first birth where he'd assisted independently. 'It's rare to have to do an episiotomy, and when it does occur an audit follows because there needs to be a good reason for one,' says Mark. Apart from this, everything seemed to be going well for a beautiful birth. 'But call it midwives' intuition, I felt something was wrong and when the baby was born he wouldn't breathe.' The baby was born pale and floppy. 'He just would not breathe so I quickly moved him to the infant Resuscitaire and pressed the emergency buzzer,' Mark says. 'People came from everywhere and quickly alerted the neonatal team in the adjoining nursery. Suddenly the situation moved from a calm, relatively straightforward birth environment to that of bright lights, cold steel and action stations. This was not how I had experienced birth over my student years. Far from it. I was like a rabbit in headlights. I was trying to explain what was going on to the woman and trying to birth the placenta. It was noisy, crazy, organised chaos.'

The baby was gently placed on the hard hospital grade surface under the radiant warmer. 'It smelled like heated disinfectant – you know that hospital-grade cleanliness.' Mark says. He was sweating from nervous tension, which was exacerbated by the strong heaters turned on to keep the baby warm. Mark quickly rubbed the baby with firm but gentle, tactile stimulation, hoping against all hope this would help the baby to breathe. But it was ineffective. With trembling hands he positioned the baby to try to open his airway to artificially breathe life into him. The neonatal team arrived with a bustle of stainless-steel trolleys carrying more advanced life-saving equipment. 'I still remember the more experienced neonatal nurse expertly and calmly guiding me aside. Her movements implied *I've got this.*'

The four responders pounced on the baby. Alarms buzzed and then life-saving orders and options were firmly uttered. Fluorescent lights flood-lit the area, gloves snapped and drawers were flung open as the neonatal resuscitation team expertly flicked through the sterile, plastic artificial airways.

Quietness followed as the paediatrician guided a small thin tube into the baby's mouth and into his lungs. Everyone's breath caught – *had this extremely difficult intervention been successful? Would the baby's lungs be flooded with much-needed oxygen, allowing the floppy, now translucent blue little boy a chance at life?*

He is pinking up, Mark said looking at the dangerously low red numbers on the monitor click in an upwards motion switching to orange and then finally green. 'It hit 90 and then the alarms went silent and the lights stopped flashing. We all looked at each other tensely. Time had stopped. It felt like an hour, but in reality it was a millisecond; each of us in the room knew the unspoken truth. Things were bad.'

The moment was broken by the neonatal nurse redirecting the team to what came next. 'I couldn't believe things could change in an instant like that,' Mark says. The baby survived the initial resuscitation but care was withdrawn a couple of days later and he died. Mark was devastated. After two years of training and not experiencing a neonatal death, it had happened on his first day on the job. 'That was really tough,' he recalls. 'I was given a lot of support and this is when midwives really come to the forefront. They gathered around me and knowing I was extremely upset, they helped me. Every midwife has a similar story. For me it came back to that power of womanhood and mothering. I visited the baby each day and cried with the parents. I wasn't there when the baby died, that was their time, but I saw them afterwards.'

The day before the baby died a CAT scan showed he had suffered a major brain haemorrhage and he wasn't able to breathe for himself. At this stage Mark didn't know when or how the baby had haemorrhaged. As the business of the hospital hurried on, Mark was beating himself up, trying to work out what he'd missed. 'I went over and over my notes and thought, *Could I have done something differently? Was there something I could have picked up on earlier that was suggestive of an intrauterine foetal brain haemorrhage?*' He had to wait for investigations and a post-mortem to determine the cause of death.

It was only when the post-mortem result came out about six months later that it was found the baby had suffered a haemorrhage, which had happened some time after the eighteen-week scan and before the birth. 'The prolonged period of waiting to find out was a big knock to my confidence and triggered a huge amount of self-doubt as a new graduate. I worried that I'd done something wrong. It was very difficult to go back in and work with another woman the next day without being overly cautious. And I could only imagine the agony and frustration the parents must have felt during the prolonged wait.

'Midwives talk about working in a wellness model – working with well women and low-risk birthing. It was hard for me for quite a while not to over-treat. I kept thinking *it might happen again.*'

It took Mark a long time to conquer that over-cautiousness. He couldn't relax and was afraid of becoming complacent. He dreaded being caught out by another surprise. 'I'd seen sick babies and a whole gamut of complications that had been picked up throughout pregnancies, but after that baby died, I lost my faith in the power of the birthing process. It eventually came back and I realised knocks like that were part of the fabric of midwifery. I still remember the baby's name and every now and then when I see a bottle of champagne, I think about that unopened bottle sitting in the mother's room. I like to think she would have gone on to have more healthy babies.'

Mark grew up in the close-knit community of Clermont and attended the local high school. Clermont is a small agricultural town with a population of 2200 in Queensland's Isaac Region, 274 kilometres south-west of Mackay. The district is home to some of Australia's most valuable mixed farming and cattle-producing country as well as being a major hub for large coalmines.

In 1992, at ten years of age, Mark suffered a ruptured appendix and was raced off from Clermont to the Mackay Base Hospital in central Queensland by air ambulance. Needing surgery, he had a prolonged stay. He says the experience sparked his interest in health care and the idea of becoming a nurse, doctor or midwife with an aeromedical organisation. He hung on to that ambition.

As a teen, the signs of his pending career were not hard to spot. When his family's cat was locked up waiting to be spayed, Mark was desperate for her to have kittens. 'I may have let her out for fifteen minutes before my parents got home from work,' he admits. 'And surprise, surprise, the cat had an immaculate conception and gave birth, with my help, to a litter of kittens.'

When Mark was in high school he let a local midwife and close family friend Marg Schifcofske know he was interested in nursing. Over the years Marg became a mentor and key role model to Mark. After a 40-year career in nursing and midwifery, she retired in 2015 and to this day the two have remained friends. Recently Mark flew to Clermont for Marg's 60th birthday.

Marg remembers when Mark came to the hospital for work experience. 'He was just so loveable. He was considerate of everyone, funny and smart. He watched his first delivery with me and another midwife. He was over the moon. It was unusual for a male student to be so interested in nursing and Mark had an unquenchable thirst for learning. He soaked up everything we shared with him. Back then there was always a bit of a stigma about male nurses. But he did so well with us girls.'

Academically Mark excelled. 'He was one these nurses that had brains as well as bedside manner,' Marg adds. Initially, when Mark let Marg know he was interested in becoming a nurse or a doctor, she tried to talk him out of it. It was in the late nineties, when birthing services in Queensland were on the decline and Clermont was facing the loss of its birthing facility. There was a doctors' crisis, rural medical services were cut and centralised and the insurance crisis was going on. Marg was feeling a bit jaded with it all.

But Mark loved what she did. 'She was a big hero of mine,' he says. 'There were other midwives in Clermont, too, a group of them, who I had quite a close relationship with – mostly through the swimming club, and they all helped guide me on my path to nursing.' At fifteen, Mark volunteered at the Clermont Hospital for work experience. 'I got to watch the birth of a baby,' he says. 'It left me with a new respect for the power of womanhood and the miracle of life. The woman gave birth without pain relief or fuss. It was completely natural and straightforward. It was the biggest defining event in my career – even though I didn't have one at that stage. It was one of the most amazing things I'd ever seen and I was hooked from then on. I love how with just one breath a whole new person enters the world and instantly becomes a major part of a family.'

At first, Mark considered becoming an orthopedic surgeon, but when he saw the birth of that baby, it changed his career aspirations. He was set for nursing and midwifery. 'I could see they were the ones that got to work and interact closely with the patients.' In the following year he volunteered to work at the hospital in his own time, outside school hours. 'When a baby was about to be born, the midwives used to call me in. I saw a couple of caesarians and natural births. The doctor was also really good to me and tried to talk me into becoming a doctor instead of a midwife. But back then to gain a medical degree in Queensland you had to do a non-medical undergraduate course first. So all the advice was to get a nursing degree in order to have a reasonable-paying job to pay for the medical degree later.'

Mark attended the University of Southern Queensland in Toowoomba to gain his three-year nursing degree. 'I did do some bush practicals, knowing the variety and experience would be greater – more births, more of everything, and I loved that. Nursing and midwifery mean working across the life span, being able to do it all.' Mark did his graduate year at St Andrews in Toowoomba on the Darling Downs and then went to the Cairns Hospital. In Cairns he did his Master of Midwifery.

As a male midwife Mark stood out. 'If I did something or said something wrong I'd hear about it,' he quips. 'One night a woman having difficulty feeding her baby was at her wit's end after trying for days. I truly believe breast is best, but sometimes there can be a pragmatic approach to facilitate this. I had to go through a massive rigmarole to get some formula. It was locked up and I had to get consent. But when you've got a tired mum who has a difficult transition to early parenting, the last thing that going to help is stringing out her anxiety. In the end I just said, *We're going to get some formula and we're going to feed and settle this baby.* Which we did. After some sleep and a settled child, we were able to get the mother to establish breastfeeding and she left the hospital a more confident mum. However, it was a huge deal. When I came back in after my days off, the lactation consultant headed straight for me. She'd been told the male midwife gave the baby the bottle. I was in for it. She said I was representing the patriarchy and had failed in my duty as a midwife … blah, blah. I stood my ground and just said, *No, I think it was the best thing for that baby.* And I asked how we could work together from this point on to help this particular woman.

'Acutely aware of my gender, generally I go out of my way to win over trust. Women would say things like, *Oh the male midwife didn't make me do that,* or nurses would say, *I don't know what you've done to her, but she won't listen to me, she wants to do it your way.* My practice was very visible. Midwifery is very political and tied up in women's rights. There are a lot of very passionate midwives and with that comes a lot of healthy debate about what's right and what's not.'

Moving to Cairns to work was a whole new state of play for Mark. 'Cairns is a tropical gem fringed with palm trees in the midst of the luscious green wet tropics,' Mark says. 'White deserted beaches, aquamarine water and of course, right beside the Great Barrier Reef. The city is a melting pot of humanity – all cultures, young sea-changers like me and a large population of Indigenous people. It is a tourist mecca – a little bit like South East Asia but with the beautiful Aboriginal Torres Strait Islander culture.'

Growing up in Clermont Mark was used to living in dry, black soil plains. He was also used to a searing dry heat where long spells of over 40 degrees was commonplace. He wasn't prepared for Cairns' high humidity and incredible rainfall. 'Arriving in January it was muggy and sweltering hot. I remember the monsoonal rain on the first day I was at the hospital and wishing some of the downpour could go further west to break the drought.'

In Cairns after graduation, Mark took part in Team Midwifery. When a woman goes into labour a midwife she has met during previous months assists her. 'It begins at antenatal classes when the pregnant woman is not in a vulnerable state. At that stage she could just get to know me as Mark rather than as the male midwife. It was a great idea.'

One of the most influential midwives Mark has worked with is Kelly Kearns. 'She was my supervisor and nominated herself to supervise a male as she thought it would be a challenge,' he says. 'I did a lot of supervised prac with Kelly and she taught me how to practise in different environments, particularly midwifery care in high-risk and obstetric situations.'

Kelly remembers the day she was asked to supervise Mark. 'I'm very traditional and dead against men in the birth suite,' she says. 'I think the birthing place is for women only and for the woman giving birth to have four or five women around her for that long labour, to rub her back and to offer that support.'

When Kelly received an email from a midwifery educator asking her to mentor a new midwife in training she was more than happy to do so. 'I love mentoring students and getting them before they touch the ground,' she says. 'I'm a good teacher on the floor. *Yes please*, I said, *send me the student's details*. But when the email came back and read, *The student I'm giving you is named Mark Holmes*, I thought, *Oh my God, she's given me a man. She knows how I feel about men in the birthing suite*. I was gutted. *I've got to train up a bloody man.*

But I couldn't get out of it. I took Mark on and yes, we made him a midwife. He actually had a fantastic rapport with the women. With the first birth we did I noticed how well he got on with the woman. We did a year together and he's gone on to do remarkable things in midwifery. He has a natural empathy and connection with women – the essential criteria for a midwife.'

One day in Cairns a young girl had developed pre-eclampsia. 'When you have high blood pressure and a number of other complications, the biggest fear is the woman will have a seizure. This girl was so young and past her due date. She was induced and with excessively high blood pressure, she needed immediate medication management. Then she had to go onto an infusion to maintain the blood pressure and then an oxytocin drip to progress her labour. She ended up having an epidural – so there was a lot going on for her.'

In the context of midwifery practice, this was very abnormal. But it was a good case of an excellent team of obstetricians and others working together to help her. 'She was very unwell and had to have a lot of medication,' Mark explains. As he watched her sitting there with several infusion devices and lit up like a Christmas tree, he realised this kind of situation took a huge amount of care. 'It's easy to just look after the machines and focus on baby vitals and numbers, but what Kelly showed me this day was to bring in the midwifery side of things. Which meant not "nursing" the machines, being task oriented and ticking things off, but instead putting the woman at the centre of the care, speaking with her, making her an active participant and applying midwifery knowledge to a high-risk obstetric situation. It means using our knowledge of how best to get the most out of the woman during birth – for example we know the best position to facilitate the descent of a baby is upright.

We try to normalise and minimise the obstetric intervention along with supporting and educating the woman to empower her to tap into her intuitive knowledge.'

The girl was extremely scared and relatively health illiterate. With Kelly's guidance, Mark explained to her what was happening. Because she was high risk, there was a big medical team hovering around and most were keen to perform a caesarian. Mark could see the girl was terrified at the thought of having an operation. 'So we worked hard, call it midwifery guardianship if you like, to fend people off and maintain safety and progression. Kelly changed the girl's position with an epidural in. It was the first time I'd seen a woman with an epidural moved to another position other than being recumbent with monitors on. Kelly got her onto her feet, propped her up so her uterus didn't have to work as hard when it contracted and rose up. An upright position taps into the power of gravity and this helps to use the woman's innate ability to birth despite her being unwell and at the end of a lot of medical intervention. It moved the woman back into a role of power and allowed her to re-own the birth.'

Mark forced himself to stay calm and collected. 'I thought, *I'm just like the fifteen-year-old girl – absolutely terrified*. I had come from a nursing background where multiple infusions didn't scare me, but I had no idea that managing the workflow could be like this.'

At the time the student midwives had to follow a certain amount of women through their care from antenatal to postnatal – and this girl was one of Mark's follow-throughs. 'We were monitoring the baby with a CTG monitor, constantly listening to the baby's heart rate and we had cardiac monitoring on to watch mum's heart rate because drugs can affect cardiac rhythms. Plus we had the epidural management and other medication, infusion and maintenance going on. Up to this point I'd only seen upright, beautiful natural births on work experience. I'd studied and heard about dramas, but this was the first time I'd gained an appreciation of things going wrong.'

Mark had never seen so much fear in anyone as this girl and it frightened him. His job was to lessen her fear and not show his. 'I thought, *We have to reassure her.* We had to get ourselves over a really complex situation and keep advocating for her. She had moved from a hard-working, active birth to sitting on the bed, quiet and still. Thankfully, things progressed well from there and the baby birthed without the caesarian and mother and child were fine. I followed the mum through and watched her take to early parenting. I had formed preconceptions in my mind – but she made a fantastic mother and did amazingly well considering her young age.'

It was then that Mark understood the importance of midwifery. 'For the first time I saw the difference between a midwife and a nurse. It went way beyond what I knew in nursing and crossed into that whole midwifery realm. I still think about it to this day and have since presented the case at a midwifery conference to highlight the value of a midwifery partnership in high-risk obstetrics.'

Kelly was very passionate about water birth and was instrumental in introducing it to Cairns at the time. Pregnant women had started asking for them. And while there was quite a bit of scepticism from hospital management and some obstetricians, it was all about providing the option. Kelly taught Mark how to do it. 'To birth underwater is an incredible thing and it's a great option in hospitals now. In low light, a warm room and warm water, the atmosphere is beautiful. The woman is completely immersed and her partner can hop in as well.'

Mark completed the qualification process to attend water births and had assisted at one before the opportunity came for him to be part of his first independent water birth. 'It was a 23-year-old woman, about my age, at the time, and she didn't want to have a traditional birth. She presented in a well-established labour and hopped into the birth pool. Blanketed and soothed by the water, she really went into herself – almost a meditative state. I knew my role was to be a fly on the wall as much as possible – an active inactivity. I just quietly checked every now and then that things were going along well. Midwives are encouraged to knit or crochet to keep their hands busy. Nurses are very task oriented, always needing something to do. So sitting and watching and staying in the background can be hard. There's a real urge to brush hair, wipe brows, provide food, make beds – do fiddly stuff. But the woman is best left alone. The midwife's role is simply to provide safety and knowledge.'

In a kneeling position in the birth pool, the woman was working hard and started pushing. 'And then very quickly she birthed a beautiful baby underwater,' Mark says. 'The baby floated to the surface with the guidance of his father. They lifted that baby out and there it was. The mum was totally in control of what was happening. She owned the birth.'

Coming from southern Queensland, Mark found the patient cases well outside his previous experience. 'It was my first major contact with the Indigenous population. Thirty-five per cent of women birthing were Aboriginal or Torres Strait Islander women and it was a huge learning curve for me.' Mark soon realised there were vast differences between Indigenous communities. 'The girls from the coast are a little more outgoing than those from places further west, like Aurukun. Those that come in from very isolated communities are harder to establish a rapport with. They're more reserved, quiet and avoid eye contact. They just needed to be left alone to do their own thing.

'The birth suite at the Cairns Hospital looks over the esplanade with stunning sea views. The islanders waiting in the maternity ward for babies would predict the sex based on the tide. I can't remember the exact detail but it was something like; if the tide was coming in when the baby was being born, it was going to be a boy. If it was going out, they would expect a girl. I think they were right 90 per cent of the time.

'I loved working with the Thursday Island women. The ward would often be packed to the rafters with aunts and older women and was a sea of colour with brightly coloured, tropical muu-muus, dresses and shirts. There would be up to eight aunties in a corner, knitting or sewing. And the families from Papua New Guinea would gather around chewing betel nut. As an outsider both culturally and genderwise, I saw that their approach was tied to the land – and most importantly, to the sea. The young mother is physically surrounded by a ring of women attending her every need. They tap into the power and wisdom of motherhood built through the generations. When it is the birthing woman's time the women congregate and celebrate womanhood and this rite of passage. It is calm and laidback with all the older, experienced women supporting the younger girl through the experience. Words of wisdom, encouragement, chatting, feeding, watering is all going on and amid the caring everyone is regularly looking out the window keeping an eye on the tide and the weather. Occasionally there is some low soft singing or humming. Always smiles, always touch, a hug and then a stern but warm "get on with it". I always felt very privileged to be among it all – a rare visitor. We were just there to make sure everything was okay and to complete the reams of paperwork that come with birthing in a hospital. As far as birthing went, we'd just let the mothers do their thing, and the majority of the time, beautiful babies were born naturally and stress free.

'There are some amazing midwives in Cairns, and while it was challenging at times, I learned a great deal. I sometimes challenged the status quo. As a male midwife, there was a reasonable amount of suspicion from the women midwives. Midwives in general can be quite tough on each other.'

Going out of his way to offset the gender difference meant Mark didn't have any trouble gaining acceptance by the mothers in his care. 'Birthing is so rooted in womanhood and women's liberation and feminism,' he explains. 'Particularly with some cultures that believe it's very much women's business only. Muslim women and some Aboriginal women stipulate birthing is women's business and it's about the spirit of what it means to be a woman going through the experience and it requires privacy. That did present a few challenges and occasionally we had to rearrange mothers and midwives to make sure we respected any cultural sensitivity. But by and large, there are no major concerns with the women I work with.' The feedback Mark receives is testimony that he is extremely aware and astute when it comes to maintaining a woman's dignity. 'Most midwives are naturally at ease with women, whereas I feel I need to go out of my way and spend time to build that relationship. That's if I have a chance. Often it's not easy, because when a woman is well into labour anything can impact on the birth environment. It's in those early labour stages or inductions you can build some trust and respect with the woman and her partner. Then it's all about maintaining those relationships.'

Mark's career in Cairns was cut short when personal tragedy struck. 'I was 23 and my partner, Alistair Frame, died suddenly overnight. He was 26. My life changed that day when I woke up, rolled over and discovered Ali had died in the night, in bed beside me. All I wanted to do was go home to Mum and Dad, which I did, and I worked in Clermont for the next twelve months. Luckily, it wasn't difficult to get a job at the hospital and it was comforting to come home and work alongside Marg and all the people I knew working there. I did some antenatal clinics, working with the local doctors' surgery and a little maternity work at Emerald to keep my midwifery current.'

Marg said everyone was delighted when Mark came back to Clermont to nurse for a twelve-month stint – and with midwifery under his belt. 'He was hilarious and brought such a sparkle to the place. He'd organise wheelchair races in the middle of the night up and down the corridor to keep the nurses awake. And he's a great dancer. His parents ran the debutante balls and when we weren't busy, he'd teach us to dance.'

Mark suddenly found himself looking after and caring for girls he had gone to school with. 'It was interesting to say the least,' he says, laughing. 'I got to know them more than I ever thought I would. But that was actually beautiful and now, ten years later, I see some of the babies I helped birth popping up on Facebook. I remember looking after them in postnatal care. We had a really nice group of core midwives for antenatal and postnatal care. We put a system in place to help women return home from regional hospitals a lot faster. Unfortunately, women could no longer birth in Clermont, so we did a lot of transfers in the back of ambulances with women in labour to Emerald, our nearest large centre, an hour south. It was crazy. That's still an area of contention for me. That part of central Queensland just seems to get forgotten by the Queensland government. You can birth in the bigger centres, but services don't go into the smaller communities – they have to go without facilities. If you want to have a baby you have to wait at one of the larger centres and birth away from home.'

Mark remembers a transfer in the back of an ambulance with a woman in labour who had had several babies. 'I tried to convince doctors to let her stay in town because I didn't think she'd make it. But we were pushed into a pretty hairy ride driving very, very fast. Strapped in, we were rocketing along the dodgy, potholed road at 140 kilometres per hour and in fading twilight – roo time.' Mark was imagining birthing scenarios. The woman, strapped down for safety, was squirming around trying to move to a more upright position. She was extremely uncomfortable. 'All the while I was flailing, grabbing on for dear life and trying to document what I was doing. I was caring for the woman and supporting her through contractions, monitoring the baby's heartbeat and hoping we didn't crash! We were both powerless and desperately wanting a normal situation – we just had to ride it out.' The woman birthed the baby about half an hour after arrival at the hospital. 'It was a lovely birth and she was back with us the next morning, where we could continue to look after her.'

On another night the hospital staff had a surprise birth when a woman who was travelling and staying at the caravan park showed up at the door. Shortly after, she birthed the baby and Mark was there to catch him. 'He was rugged up, cuddling and breastfeeding with his mother when the doctor who had been called raced in sounding out orders and calling for drugs. He was surprised to find the baby already nuzzling at the breast, skin-to-skin, cuddling with mum and dad. They were in low, soft light and it was absolutely beautiful. The baby pretty much birthed himself.'

In midwifery, the term 'delivery' isn't used anymore because it implies the woman is passive during delivery. 'Pizzas get delivered, not babies,' Mark says. 'They get birthed. And we don't refer to women as patients – they are women.'

After a year of healing and spending time with family and friends in Clermont, Mark headed off to Scotland and took a break from midwifery. He had the opportunity to do some maternity-care assistance and shifts in the birthing suites in Edinburgh. 'I'd worked in much smaller environments and to go to a major tertiary referral centre was a bit of a shock. I kept in mind the first birth I'd seen and compared everything with that. To this day that's still how I think it should be done – with no bells and whistles.'

Mark fell into emergency nursing in the Western General Hospital mainly because that's all that was going. 'It was a very big change for me. At that stage it was almost impossible to register as an Australian-trained midwife in the UK. To get in as a nurse I had to sit an English-language test at considerable expense.

'When I first moved to Cairns I worked in surgical wards and I had seen a reasonable amount of drug and alcohol related trauma there. However substance abuse in Scotland was a very big thing. It was a great experience working across three big hospitals. I gained a lot of new skills and exposure to different cultures. I knew nothing about Eastern European culture and all that went with that.'

Mark worked in Edinburgh for a couple of years until the global financial crisis hit and the National Health Service (NHS) stopped renewing visas for foreign workers. 'There were no more jobs and they sent us all home.' His long-term plan to get into aeromedical nursing was suddenly on the cards. 'These days the only real way to practise nursing and midwifery side by side is in aeromedical or to take a placement in a rural or remote area. Mindful of the smaller birthing units closing around the country, I decided the only way to practise the two disciplines I enjoy was to become a flight nurse.' He applied to NSW Air Ambulance. 'Being a proud Queenslander and afraid of big impersonal cities, the last place I said I'd ever live was Sydney,' he says. 'I had been travelling around Queensland for six weeks with my new partner, David, who had come out from Scotland with me. We were filling in time waiting to hear about the Sydney job before deciding where to head next if I didn't get it. When I did get it, I thought, *I'll just see how it goes for six months.*' Seven years later he's still in the job and loving it. 'I have all the conveniences of living in Sydney while I'm working in the bush.'

Mark had applied for the NSW Air Ambulance job two months before he left Scotland to return to Australia. 'At last I was going for the flying job I'd wanted for so long. I knew I'd need a lot of experience to get it and didn't think I'd have much of a chance. We arrived back in Australia in April and still hadn't heard anything. The recruitment period took about three months back then so we decided to take off on a six-week road trip around Queensland. It was a great way to show David the country. We were having an amazing time on the Great Barrier Reef when I got the phone call. They said, *Congratulations, you've got the job. Can you be in Sydney on Tuesday?* It was Friday. I said, *Yes, no problem.* I hung up and in full snorkelling gear on the Low Isles, told David we had to be in Sydney by Tuesday. And David, not realising the full scale of Australia, raised his eyebrows and nodded approval. He didn't have a driving licence, so I drove all the way. We rocked up with our seventeen kilograms of luggage and nowhere to live.'

Mark was 26 years old when he started the job in 2009 – the youngest flight nurse they'd ever employed. 'I started while David found us an apartment. Our funds were running dry, but he found a furnished place. I was flying and not contactable most of the time. I came home one day and he said he'd found us an amazing apartment. We moved in. We were smack bang in the middle of Kings Cross in a back alley near all the night-clubs and several brothels nearby. It was a huge eye-opener for us. We'd sit on our rooftop terrace and watch drug deals below. At the time they were filming the TV series, *Underbelly*. There was a lot going on. Two and a half years later we moved to the port side of Kings Cross to Rushcutters Bay, just 500 metres down the hill. It's on Sydney Harbour and it's a place we love.'

Mark settled quickly into his new job as a flight nurse. 'I absolutely loved it. I hadn't been aware of how much train-ing was needed to become part of an aeromedical team. I'd always been a bit of an aviation geek and plane spotter and I think it helped me get the job when I told them my story about being flown to Mackay in the air ambulance. At first I was geo-graphically challenged. I was flying around not knowing what part of New South Wales I was in. We were flying to places like Bourke, Lightning Ridge, Walgett, Mungindi, Ivanhoe, Griffith, Tumut, Dubbo, Mudgee, Orange, Forbes and Parkes. Most of the calls for midwifery would come from the state's north-west due to the lack of services out there. The Indigenous moth-ers would present late for antenatal care. Understandably they preferred to birth on country. We would fly out to help birth their babies or retrieve women that needed assistance.'

Mark was in western New South Wales on a job once and just happened to be in the hospital when the midwife asked if he'd mind answering a buzzer while she went off to do some-thing else. He walked into the ward and found it was the birth suite with a woman in the throes of birthing her baby. 'Within minutes I had a baby in my hands and handed it to the mother. She said, *Who are you?*

'*The gardener*, I said with a big grin. I was in uniform but she didn't appreciate my humour and I had to promptly explain I was actually a midwife.'

As NSW Air Ambulance is an emergency service, the vast majority of call-outs involve high-risk, medical trauma and other serious cases. The majority of patients are transferred to a high level of care.

For example, most of the women Mark worked with were those experiencing high blood pressure in pregnancy, premature labour or other complications. There were also those few term women that refused to travel long distance to have their babies. 'Women are sent from their communities for the sit-down period to wait at the larger centre for the baby to be born, which could be from four to six weeks. Many have to pay for accommodation and it becomes an expensive wait. So it's understandable that many don't want to go off country. Instead, they present late, when the ship has already sailed. It can be hard to convince women to take a plane and head for a city when at home they are surrounded by extended family – aunts, sisters and grandparents. This includes Indigenous and non-Indigenous women. Birthing on country applies to everyone. Girls from my school in Clermont can't birth there anymore either. They, too, have an attachment to the land and their home. It's not fair on them.'

One night Mark flew to the high altitude ranges of central New South Wales for a woman in premature labour with twins. In sleet and snow, they brought her out to the aircraft. 'She was having contractions, but I decided it would be safe to set off for a 40-minute flight,' he says. 'Just before take-off we got a call asking if we could hold because they had someone with a bleed on their brain coming in from another small town further west and needing to see a neurosurgeon in Sydney.

With two stretchers on the plane, we had room so we waited. I had the woman expecting twins up front and when the other woman arrived in the ambulance we made the decision to walk her up the stairs instead of using the stretcher because she looked okay and it would be faster and warmer for her. As she reached the top of the stairs she had a major seizure. The brain bleed had extended. Then suddenly the pregnant woman told me she wanted to push and that the first baby was on the way. So while I'm attending the lady having a seizure, doing all I needed to do putting airways in and dealing with a brain bleed, I'm calling out to the other woman, *It's alright, breathe through it, I'll be with you in a minute.* Luckily the paramedic crew was still there. When the woman with the seizure was stable again, they took her to the regional referral centre, where she was put on life support and evacuated later. I headed off to Sydney after assessing the pregnant woman to make sure the babies weren't coming right then and there and elected to go. The twins were born within an hour after arriving in Sydney.'

When Mark started as a flight nurse in 2009 he called one of his best friends, Amanda Bianchi, at the end of a tough retrieval job. The two had grown up in Clermont together. Amanda's phone rang at 2 am and Mark was on the other end sobbing. 'He rarely breaks down so I knew it was a big deal. *Just breathe*, I said. *Is everyone okay? What's going on?* He told me he'd just got home. He had been tasked to fly out to a remote area to retrieve a labouring woman pregnant with twins at 26 weeks. Mark stabilised her for the flight, but midway she started to bleed. He was working on his own and had to care for the mother and her babies independently. The mother was bleeding and the babies were in great danger. There he was caring for the three of them on his own. I asked him how it ended. He said, *I got them all off the plane alive – with both babies in utero and the mother stable.* But it had completely drained him. He'd given everything he had to give. He kept saying, *Don't tell anyone I called you, I have to do a debrief.* I just said, *Honey, I am your debrief. And you can hold this story up high.* He was in his mid-twenties and he saved three lives that night.'

NSW Air Ambulance base executive assistant Suzanne Bristow is one of Mark's closest work colleagues. She says that as an elite flight nurse, Mark is exceptional in what he does. 'Everybody loves him,' she says. 'There are not many flight nurses in the world. They are looking after patients in the sky without a doctor. To get to this level they have to be the best at what they do. Not too many come with the entire package. There's a lot of training involved and Mark has clocked up some wonderful achievements, including raising the profile of flight nurses through his role as president with Flight Nurses Australia. He knows how to read people and how to deal with them and is very professional in his work. He has a way with patients and is extremely generous in nature with whomever he is dealing with. His compassion shines through and patients and pregnant women love him. I don't know where he finds the hours to do all he does. It's not just his job he gives one hundred per cent to, he does a lot of vital voluntary work in rural and remote areas.'

On 23 May 2015 Mark and David were legally married in Edinburgh. 'Mum and Dad came as well as a bunch of my friends. A few months later we had a reception, for want of a better word, in Sydney so more of our Australian friends could celebrate with us.'

Three years ago Mark moved into an education role with NSW Air Ambulance and does fifty-fifty flying and ground-based education. As a flight nurse/midwife educator he teaches new recruits, predominantly on the midwifery side, and makes training videos. Using a simulator he teaches crew in a replica aircraft cabin complete with camera, microphones and intercom. 'We close students in and put them through scenarios while we watch from another room. Then we debrief them – there's a very strong educational framework behind it. It could be a postpartum haemorrhage, involving a lot of fake blood that we simulate, and the classroom is in the air.'

Mark has also joined the Council of Remote Area Nurses of Australia (CRANAplus), which runs maternity, emergency, and midwifery upskilling courses around the country and educates, supports and represents all health professionals working in Australia's remote sector. On a voluntary basis and on his days off he facilitates on four three-day courses a year. 'It takes education to the people, not vice versa, and we go to far-flung places across Australia to deliver maternal courses to places like Roma, Blackall, Katherine, Darwin, Alice Springs and Western Australia. I like to think I can inspire some non-midwives to consider midwifery and take it back to their local communities. I've managed to convert a few to take it on as a career. Birthing in the bush is much better because they are almost always natural. I like to get on my high horse about the closure of birthing facilities in rural and remote communities. So much of my formative years were in the country and this is a great way to give a bit back.'

Mark was the first male student to go through the University of Southern Queensland as a midwife and the first male midwife in the Cairns Hospital for many years. He was the 110th male midwife to register in Queensland. Today, men make up about 10.5 per cent of the nursing workforce and only one per cent of registered midwives.

6

Joy Motter

Joy Motter was sound asleep in the nurses' quarters at the Fitzroy Crossing Hospital when at 2.30 am a loud bang on the door woke her. Instinctively, she knew something was wrong. She opened the door to find Barry, the teacher from the Aboriginal school based on a cattle station twenty kilometres away. He was with Martin, an Aboriginal man who worked on the station. 'You're needed,' Barry said anxiously. 'Martin's wife has gone into labour and is in a lot of pain. Can you come?'

Responding at once, Joy picked up her maternity bundle and hastily packed drugs from the fridge. From the grounds of the small remote hospital in the West Kimberley region, she walked briskly behind two men across the hospital lawn down to the river. She knew they'd have to cross the water to get to a waiting Jeep. Joy hadn't had to do this at night before and tried not to think too much about the risks or voice her concern.

'It was the wet season and I knew we'd have to wade across a knee-deep, croc-infested, rushing river. I thought, *Oh God, the current will be strong enough to wash us away.*'

The only thing in their favour was a full moon. In pale, luminous light they could make out the Jeep on the other side. Martin entered the water first. Joy paddled in closely behind him, firmly gripping the belt around his shorts, and Barry scruffed the back of Joy's shirt as they moved. In this makeshift lifeline and against a strong current, the three strode across, clinging to each other. In was 1968 and Joy was 24 years old.

When they arrived at the station, Joy followed Martin and Barry up to the men's kitchen at the main building where the manager lived. She worried about what she might find. 'I thought, *I'll have to clear all the men out and deal with this as best I can,*' Joy says. She knew Martin's wife. She had seen her recently at the hospital for an antenatal check and knew this would be an early delivery.

'Sally had been taken from the camp up to the cook's quarters. The cook was the only other woman on the station at the time and she had tried to make Sally comfortable. During the wet season the women took off,' Joy says. It was 3.30 am by the time Joy reached the expectant mother. 'She was lying on the bed in the men's kitchen. The long-time station manager was up and having coffee. He was the boss of everyone and he "needed" to know about everything that happened. He was grumpy and asked me what was going on. I knew I'd have to be firm with him. *Just stay out of the way. I'll deal with it. Just leave me alone and everything will be fine.*'

She told everyone to stay away while she tended to Sally. 'The baby's legs were out and the head was stuck,' Joy says. When she saw this, she knew instantly that the baby had died and her heart sank. It was a breech delivery. 'I thought, *Oh dear, I'll just have to do this as best I can,*' she recalls. 'When I told Sally I would give her a needle to ease the pain, she covered her face with her hands. She didn't want to see what I was doing.' Joy knew she just had to get the baby out and try to keep the mother calm and as pain free as possible. 'I talked to her all the time, trying to keep her mind off the pain I knew she would be in.' Joy thought back to her midwifery training days, remembering a lecture that could help her. 'We were discussing breeches and difficult births one day. The lecturer said not to worry, if it ever happened, there'd be a doctor to take over. A student nurse had the sense to ask, *But what if you were in the back of New Guinea and there wasn't a doctor around? I think we should know what to do.* So the lecturer took us through the procedure.'

Then, in the tiny hours of that morning, in a remote part of Western Australia, Joy drew on those instructions. Working in the low, shimmering light of a kerosene lantern, she found the baby's head above the pelvic bone with her hand and pushed gently. Then she put her hand underneath the chin with one finger in the baby's tiny mouth and softly wriggled up and down, trying desperately not to injure the mother's birth passage. 'The largest part of the baby, which usually paves the way, was coming out last,' Joy says. 'Like the majority of Aboriginal women, this mother was incredibly stoic. She just uttered a few soft groans. There was no screaming or complaining whatsoever. When I birthed the baby, she knew it wasn't alive. I wrapped it up gently and showed Sally her baby's face. Then I placed the infant on the floor and gave Sally a needle to stop further bleeding.'

By then the sun was rising and men were trying to enter the kitchen. In no uncertain terms, Joy told them to come back later. 'Sally needed to go to the hospital. I asked the cook to make her some tea and bread and jam.' When Sally was feeling a little stronger, Martin, Barry and Joy bundled her up and settled her in the Jeep. When they reached the rising river, they realised they wouldn't be able to carry her across. 'The hospital was on the banks of the river on the other side, so we just kept beeping the horn and yelling in chorus, *Patient, police, patient, police!* Eventually one of the nurses appeared.'

To Joy's relief the police arrived at the edge of the river with the boat used during the wet season to cross. 'We got Sally back to the hospital and called the Royal Flying Doctor Service [RFDS]. But it was Good Friday and they had shut down for the long weekend. So I called around and found another pilot. He flew in and evacuated Sally and her deceased baby to our nearest regional base, Derby.' While it had been a very difficult and sad experience, Joy felt pleased with the outcome. Working levelheadedly and without panic, everything had gone to plan. She had saved Sally's life and birthed the baby without gravely injuring her.

Born in 1943, Joy grew up in the country town of Mortlake in Victoria's western district. She lived on a mixed farm with her parents, two sisters and a brother. When she finished school at sixteen she didn't know what she wanted to do. 'Mum said, *Well you're not coming home to the farm*. I didn't really want to anyway,' Joy says. She left home to board with relatives and work in an office in Warrnambool, 40 kilometres away on the coast. When she turned eighteen, she knew she wanted to become a nurse. She trained at the Warrnambool District Hospital (now called South West Healthcare Hospital) for three years and stayed on as a junior sister. 'They had a private midwifery section staffed by trained nurses. Every now and then there weren't enough on duty, and as I was working in the private patients' section and was one of the senior nurses by this stage, they called on me to help.'

One day there was a delivery in the labour ward. A nurse went to get Joy and said she was needed to hold a woman's leg. In those days, women had the option of giving birth on their side, where one leg is on the bed and the other held by someone to expose the delivery area. 'So here I was kneeling on the bed, hanging onto her leg. Sweat was pouring off my face. I'd seen births before of cattle, dogs and cats, but here was a human and I was fascinated. The doctor said, *You're sweating, are you alright?* I was sweating because the floodlight was three inches from my head and aiming at me. That was the first birth I'd participated in.' And that's when Joy knew she wanted to be a midwife.

Joy did her twelve-month midwifery training at the Royal Women's Hospital in Melbourne. 'I absolutely hated it,' she says. 'I liked looking after the mothers and babies and the women seemed to like me and could talk to me, but coming from a little country hospital I was shy and outside my comfort zone.' As soon as she passed her exam, she left Melbourne.

With midwifery training in the bag and preferring to see Australia rather than travelling overseas like so many young people had started to do, in 1966 Joy set off on a trip halfway around Australia with her friend Jenny, who was also a country girl and had trained in midwifery with her.

Afterwards she moved to Sydney to complete a child health course for six months. The yearning to find work in a remote area in Western Australia played continually on her mind. 'I had nearly completed my three nursing certificates, which was rare in those days, and I knew they could get me places. I applied to the Australian Inland Mission (AIM), run by the Presbyterian Church, for a position somewhere in the Kimberley region. A place was available at the Fitzroy Crossing Hospital. *That'll do*, I thought.' So in April 1968, at 24 years of age and unfazed by the unknown, Joy made her way to the Crossing for the start of an incredible life adventure.

Fitzroy Crossing is in the Shire of Derby, West Kimberley that covers a vast area of 118,560 square kilometres. Located more than 2000 kilometres north of Perth, there are numerous Aboriginal communities across the shire. Derby and Fitzroy Crossing are the two main towns. When Joy arrived at her new post, the Crossing was home to a largely Aboriginal population and about 40 non-Indigenous people. The Fitzroy Crossing owes its existence to the mighty Fitzroy River, which every wet season can rise to more than thirteen metres above the old concrete crossing and swell into a raging torrent. In full flood it's one of the world's largest rivers and a sight very few travellers get to see. Those that do manage to get there often have no choice but to wait at the Crossing for the water to recede. These days there's a highway and bridge further south and most of the town has shifted as a result.

'In between wet seasons the place was very dry and that's when the cattle were mustered, and tourists, if they were brave enough, would come in to the Crossing,' Joy says. 'When parts of the road were sealed from Broome to Kununurra in the 1980s, and with a well-maintained gravel road, more people ventured in, but there was never a general flow. Travel in the wet season was by plane or nothing. Even now people don't drive in the Kimberley during the wet. November was known as suicide month. Just before the wet season broke, it would be hot, sticky, no rain and full of insects – it was the worst.'

Despite the isolation and extreme weather, Joy warmed to the Crossing the minute she arrived. 'I loved it,' she says. 'I think it went well for me because I was a country girl. I could cope with it and actually enjoyed the remoteness. With a large Indigenous population, the hospital patients were mostly Aboriginal. There were also a lot of people working and living out on massive cattle stations and they supported camps for their Aboriginal workers. Most of the 40 non-Indigenous people lived and worked in the town at the school, hospital, police station, post office and hotel, and about 250 Aboriginal people lived at the United Aborigines Mission (UAM).'

The UAM was home for many Aboriginal people of different tribes who chose not to stay on cattle stations. There were two dormitories – male and female. Most of the families on cattle stations sent their children to board at the mission for their schooling and they attended the Fitzroy Crossing School, which was outside the mission boundary. The adults were involved in tending to the mission community with tasks such as rubbish removal, vegetable gardening, working in the mission store or working in the community kitchen to prepare meals for the children. Some people at the mission also worked in the wider community as housemaids, kitchen hands or yardmen. Some worked at the police station, hospital or the hotel, which also ran a store – called the pub store. Change began to take place from about 1966 when Aboriginal people were granted full citizenship Australia-wide. The Kimberley was one of the last areas for this to take place. Relationships between everyone in the community, Indigenous and non-Indigenous, were generally peaceful. 'I stayed around for another 40 years and witnessed many changes,' says Joy.

When it came to medical cases and emergencies, anything could come through the hospital doors and Joy soon got used to dealing with everything from trauma and birthing to broken bones, disease and death. 'There wasn't a doctor in town, just the nurses,' she says. 'Derby, on the coast, was our regional base. It was a 220-kilometre drive over a mostly dirt road. Our main source of medical assistance was the RFDS. If there was something we couldn't cope with we rang the doctor in Derby and he'd tell us what to do and if needed, help organise an evacuation with the RFDS. It had a base in Derby. When the plane approached we'd hear it fly over the hospital and then drive our patients down to the airstrip.'

One day, Joy's friend Virginia was on duty and helped deliver a baby. When the mother started bleeding profusely, she raced down to the quarters at three in the morning to get Joy. 'We decided to call the RFDS, who told us what to do to stem the bleeding and that they'd wait until daylight to come in. Until then we just had to keep an eye on her.' At daylight they loaded the mother into the back of a ute on a mattress and covered her in blankets, with Virginia holding up the saline bag to continue hydrating the mum during the drive. Joy wrapped up the baby and placed it on the floor in the front of the ute to keep it safe from bumps. There was no child seat. Everything was going well and they set off to the airstrip. 'This was Virginia's first drama. When we came back to the hospital and sat down for a cup of tea, grinning from ear to ear she said, *That's what I've always dreamed of. Rescuing someone in the outback*. Unique experiences like that stick in your mind.'

Once a fortnight doctors would fly into Fitzroy Crossing with the RFDS to run a clinic. 'We'd try to arrange for pregnant women to come in so a doctor could see them. If a woman was expecting her first baby, the delivery would be done in Derby with a doctor. The women didn't mind if the doctor was a male, as long as a female nurse was present. After that they could deliver in Fitzroy for the second to fifth baby, but back to Derby for any more. Almost always the system worked well and baby deliveries were trouble free.'

Lane Johnson, pictured at CareFlight base, Darwin International Airport, with pilots Ben Ragg (left) and Matthew Mommers.

This woman's waters broke on a sheep property in north-west NSW. At 30 weeks pregnant and in premature labour she needed to be flown to a tertiary facility to birth her baby and required Neonatal Intensive Care Unit (NICU) after the birth. **Mark Holmes** provided her with medical care, explained what to expect on arrival and, crucially, gave her support and reassurance. *Photo courtesy NSW Ambulance.*

Joy Motter pictured with a mother and her new baby, wrapped and resting in a coolamon (handcrafted wooden cradle). They are under a shady bough shed (made of wooden logs, spinifex and wire), where Joy ran clinics at the camp on Gogo Station, Fitzroy Crossing in 1969.

Gayle Donaldson (back row, middle) pictured at her midwifery graduation in Townsville, 1990.

Pia Croft, centre in green cardigan, pictured at The Birth House, Geelong, Victoria, with a mothers' group.

Genevieve Brideson, flight nurse and midwife with the Royal Flying Doctor Service, 2007.

Wendy Agars pictured at the Royal Flying Doctor Service (RFDS) Cairns base with pilot Ben Wilby.

Chloe Coker took this photo after Cyclone Lam on Milingimbi Island. Dry blankets were delivered to families to help keep the babies warm. From left, strong woman Julie, a young mother and her baby, a visitor from Swinburne University helping out and strong woman Judy.

Kate Austin, pictured with Beryl and her children. Beryl presented Kate with a genuine Yolngu basket – the family wanted to give Kate a present for the close, ongoing care she provided during some difficult times for Beryl.

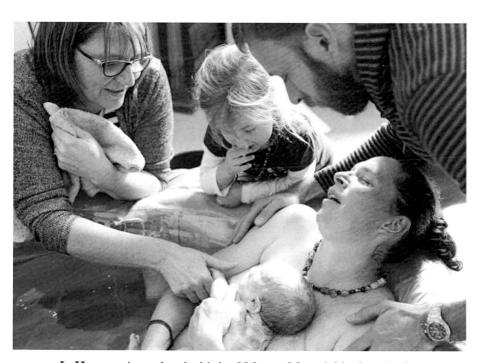

Jo Hunter pictured at the birth of Megan. Megan's big sister, Amity, watches on in wonder. *Photo by Jerusha Sutton.*

Lane Johnson, transporting baby Braxton, who had a respiratory infection, to Darwin Hospital. Photo taken by his mum (left), and on board CareFlight (right).

Lisa Peberdy, flying back to Mt Isa after a hectic clinic on Mornington Island in the Gulf of Carpentaria.

Along the Oodnadatta track to Coober Pedy – a regular Outback drive for **Marg McDonald-Ashe** to reach women on cattle stations who are under her care. *Photo by Thomas Wielecki.*

Marg McDonald-Ashe, pictured on the Birdsville Track on her way to Dulkaninna Station and Pandi Pandi Station to perform baby health checks.

Olivia Bigham pictured at Tiwi Islands taking mother and newborn baby to hospital. The baby boy was named Kevin Sylvani after the Essendon and Carlton football player and coach.

Midwife **Lisa Peberdy**, pictured in Brisbane. After many years of working in remote areas as a midwife, Lisa is now the Queensland manager of Cell Care – a national cord blood bank company. She is also completing a PhD exploring cord blood stem cell therapy and how patients, obstetricians and midwives understand it.

The RFDS centre also ran radio sessions for the community. People could switch on early each morning to send telegrams and messages. At 8 am the medical session would begin and if you needed to you could talk to the doctor. People called in from cattle stations and if the medical session wasn't on they could check telegrams. Later, the children came on for School of the Air lessons. 'It was crackly and at times out of order, but it was our lifeline of communication.'

Virginia Mitchell remembers her time working with Joy as though it were yesterday. She affectionately calls her Joybells. 'When I arrived to work with her at the hospital she met me at the airport in a troopy. I came in as a theatre nurse from Melbourne and was dressed up to the nines. I took one look at this tall, raw-boned woman and thought, *Ooh, white uniform, no veil, sleeves removed and no belt.* Her white shoes were brown and she wore no stockings – her legs were bare. We sized each other up and I thought, *Well this is clearly a place where you sink or swim. I might sink.*'

At the time, the hospital was short-staffed, so Virginia had to simply plunge in. 'The hospital ran on a generator that wasn't always on. The first delivery I did with Joybells was in lantern light and that's where I first saw just how capable this woman was. She had an extraordinary strength and confidence about her and a practical, determined nature. And she was a great and generous teacher. She'd tell me to work things out on my own, but if I had any concerns she was happy to discuss them. At the hospital we had an old kerosene fridge, our own gen set [generator] and had to start and maintain the water pump. We had to do a little of everything and we didn't really mind. Joybells had grown up on a farm and was used to it – she passed her bush skills, enthusiasm and knowledge on to me.'

With very few eligible women in the Crossing, the nurses were popular. When the river was up, people used to call in to the hospital to wait while the water receded. It was lots of fun for the two nurses. The hospital was just near the low-level crossing, where everybody who wanted to go north or south had to cross. 'People would call in, bringing us things like beef or home produce, or just wanting a cup of tea and a yarn. We weren't busy all the time, so this was a major part of our social fabric.'

Not long after her arrival, Joy met an eye-catching young stockman from one of the local cattle stations. 'Like so many of the locals, Jim popped in to the hospital to visit the nurses whenever he was in town. We just clicked,' Joy says. They married in 1970 in the grounds of the hospital. 'My older sister lived in Geelong, Victoria, and as our parents weren't able to come to the wedding, she said she'd come with her husband. She rang some friends and chartered two single-engine planes for nine passengers to fly them from Melbourne to Alice Springs.'

It's no simple thing to have a wedding in the outback. And Joy's required a joint effort that was typical of the spirit of the community. 'The planes from Melbourne arrived in Alice Springs and from there they headed into a dust storm and had to turn back,' recalls Virginia, who was Joy's bridesmaid. 'The wedding had to be delayed. The wedding cake was made in Victoria and trucked up to Kununurra, where the padre picked it up. His wife iced it and brought it to Fitzroy. A friend of mine could play the piano so we borrowed the mission's piano and drove it across to the hospital in a four-wheel-drive Toyota. The pianist was from Derby and was late arriving. Her Volkswagen had broken down and we had to send someone out to tow her in. I'd put lovely posies of flowers on tables and in trees in the hospital gardens. Someone left the gate open and the cows got in and ate them all. Then I had to find someone to shovel up all the cow dung. Finally, the wedding proceeded under the gum tree and everything was wonderful – except for the bull ants running up everyone's legs. The whole party was jumping up and down and stomping. I'd never been to a wedding like it – and haven't since. It's etched in my memory.'

When Joy and Jim married, Jim was working at Fossil Downs and they had a flat out on the station. A bit later they moved to Cherrabun Station when Jim got the manager's job there. It was 140 kilometres east of Fitzroy Crossing, and to the west, 238 kilometres from Halls Creek.

'We were based at Cherrabun from 1972 to 1989,' says Joy. 'There was a community of about 60 Aboriginal people living about fifteen kilometres from the station homestead. There was a school and with no telephone, outside communication was through high-frequency radio. I was able to strike a deal with the former West Kimberley Community Health Services to tend to the medical needs of our little community. I gave immunisations, antenatal and postnatal care, saw to injuries and illness and organised people who needed to be seen by the doctor or nurse when the RFDS plane called in for a monthly clinic. They paid me for ten hours' work a week, which also meant I could maintain my nursing registration.'

One afternoon Joy heard someone calling her name from outside near the laundry. It was Dora from the community. 'She told me her granddaughter, Shirley, was having a baby. *Where is she?* I asked her. She pointed behind the meat house – *Over there*. We walked towards it and I could see Shirley squatting near an anthill. She was definitely in labour. I hadn't known she was pregnant and asked her if it was too early. She said it was. Dora and I walked her towards the house, but only got as far as the shady lawn by the men's kitchen. *It's coming*, said Shirley.'

The laundry was close, so Joy grabbed two old towels and a bucket of water to wash her hands. She placed one towel beneath Shirley and one to cover her body just before the baby was born. But as soon as it was birthed, Joy realised that the baby wasn't alive. She ran quickly to the homestead to get the necessary gear from her medical box – scissors, cord clamp, a syringe to give Shirley a shot to prevent bleeding and some clean sheets. The placenta expelled and Joy gave the injection. 'I wrapped the baby in some sheets and asked Shirley if she wanted to see her baby's body. She said, *Only the head.* Dora and I took the baby to the laundry and sadly inspected the tiny body. It was perfectly formed but quite premature. I firmly wrapped the little body, placed it in a small box and put it in the coolroom.'

Dora and Joy helped Shirley walk to the verandah and on to a stretcher bed. 'I went inside and made a cup of tea for the three of us. Then I contacted the RFDS operator in Derby and spoke to the doctor. Two hours later the plane flew in to collect Shirley and the deceased baby.'

Joy thrived on station life. 'I'm a people person and here I was on a remote station with a whole lot of people and a community to care for. Jim had worked through the ranks and made manager. So we were living in the big house – not real flash, but we were comfortable.' To avoid the heat everyone got up at 4 am to get the work done. It was too hot for horse and cattle work during the day. Then rain would start coming in November, but the wettest months were February and March and they were too wet to do anything. This was when most station people took their holidays. The horses were moved to higher paddocks near the homestead to keep an eye on them and the cattle were left to their own devices. 'The middle months were really very nice. It was hot and horrible most of the time, but you learned to cope with it, even without air conditioners.'

The camps had bough sheds made out of dried spinifex. It was stacked between two layers of wire netting to form walls around a cement floor. Then a tin roof was added with more spinifex on the top. A hose running around the roof and on top of the walls dripped water down the spinifex, making it breezy and cool inside. Most stations had a generator for power, but these were used only for emergencies. Everyone had kerosene fridges and wooden stoves.

'One day when we were having trouble with the kerosene fridge yet again, I rang head office to let them know I wanted an electric fridge,' Joy says. 'To my surprise and delight, they sent me one.'

On the one-million-acre station there was plenty of cattle work. There were two stock camps with a non-Indigenous head stockman and assistant head stockman in each camp. All other station workers were Aboriginal. 'Jim would tell the head stockman what work was to be done and he in turn would work with his men.' The method largely worked well and the operation ran smoothly.

At Cherrabun the RFDS flew in once a month for a clinic. One day in July 1982, Joy introduced the doctor to Susan, a pregnant woman in the camp with three to four weeks to go before the birth of her baby. The doctor disagreed with Joy's estimated birth date and insisted Susan would be fine until the next clinic, a month away. 'I thought, *Okay, he's the boss* and let it go. Two and a half weeks later, Jim was out at a stock camp for the day and our two sons were in the schoolroom with their governess. Suddenly, I could see Elsie, an elder woman walking flat out up to the house. I thought, *Oh dear, Susan's having that baby.* We drove down to the camp and sure enough, she was in labour. Elsie had cleaned the area and Susan was lying on a swag with clean sheets. I raced back to the house and interrupted the RFDS radio session to call for the doctor. I said we had an emergency and I needed to talk to the doctor. I waited and waited. I called back. *I need the plane – she's going to deliver her baby soon.* They told me the RFDS plane was 400 kilometres away. *You're on your own.*

'We had an RFDS medical box and some bits and pieces I'd need for after delivery – antiseptics and some other basic things. Elsie and I sat with Susan and lots of other women sat outside in the shade, waiting anxiously. Susan birthed with minimal fuss. I cut the cord and wrapped the tiny baby girl in a blanket. Susan named her Veronica. I gave Susan an after-birth injection, but I was concerned about the baby. I gave her to Susan to nurse on her chest. I knew something was wrong because her little legs were floppy.' Not wanting to panic any-one, Joy said everything was okay and asked someone to make some tea. 'Susan was hungry, so I went up to the house to get her something to eat, which gave me a chance to call up the RFDS base on the radio again. They said the plane would arrive at 2 pm. I made Susan a ham sandwich and we waited patiently for the plane.'

When they heard it approaching, they bundled Susan and Veronica into the four-wheel drive and drove to the airstrip. The kids ran out of school and raced down excitedly to see the baby. As the flight sister and doctor were taking the two up the plane steps, Joy could hear a vehicle coming. '*Hang on a minute, you'd better wait*, I said. The vehicle sped on to the airstrip. Aboard was a bloke with a broken collarbone. The sister said, *Put him in* and away they went. The next morning

Susan's mother and sister came up to the homestead to find out how the baby was. RFDS had radioed in to say they were both doing well.'

After Susan and the baby had been flown in, Joy wanted to talk to the doctor. 'The radio communication was public – so you didn't discuss personal matters unless it was during a medical session when less people would be listening in.' The doctor confirmed there was something wrong with baby Veronica. She had been born with double-sided dislocated hips, which meant the ball at the top of both legs wasn't sitting in the sockets. When Susan came home Veronica was in a little brace to help relocate her hips back into the sockets. It had strapping around her body and down through the inside of her legs, pulling her knees out. Another strap went up over her shoulder, keeping her legs up and out. Joy thought this was going to be interesting. 'I thought, *How's this going to be managed?* But it's amazing how often without any intervention, things fall into place. Aboriginal women carry their babies on their hips with a leg on one side and the other at the back. Susan was comfortably broad, so when Veronica was on her hip, her legs splayed, placing each hip back in the socket. It worked. I knew the brace would be ditched, but it didn't worry me too much, because I knew Susan would carry Veronica everywhere and it would be just as effective as the brace. Before long Veronica was running around normally – the problem corrected itself.'

Years later, Joy ran into Susan and Veronica in Fitzroy. Veronica was sixteen and was holding her own brand-new baby. 'She knew I had delivered her. With a wide grin on my face I said to her baby, *I am your granny.*'

In 1983 the station owners, the Emanuel family, decided to sell their cattle stations. The process took some time and Joy and Jim decided they didn't want to work for the new owners.

'At the same time, a couple of smaller properties came on to the market through the WA government. There was nothing on them, but they were made affordable for ordinary people to buy and develop. We put in for one and got it.' Bulka Station was half a million acres and about 40 kilometres from Cherrabun as the crow flies. It was closer to Halls Creek, but 130 kilometres from Fitzroy Crossing. By this stage, Joy's son Clinton was working and John was still at school.

'Jim managed to get contract mustering work and with no house on the place I decided to go back to full-time nursing as a community health nurse in Fitzroy Crossing. I got a flat and worked five days a week, going home on weekends. I did that for the next fifteen years. It was quite different to my earlier years working at the hospital. I worked in a community and a school at Junjuwa. I held clinics, checked eyes and ears, anything that came my way. I concentrated largely on mothers and babies. Because I was a female I didn't see too many men. But most people in the community knew Jim and me and that helped. They felt quite comfortable about coming to see me and I was doing a lot of preventative work, taking blood pressures, checking baby weights, giving injections – that kind of thing.'

One morning a young girl came in to Joy for her eighteen-month immunisation needle. 'The family had been teasing her about having to have a big needle. Understandably, the child arrived kicking and screaming – she didn't want to have a needle. So her grandmother and aunty hung on to her and I gave her the needle. As soon I took it out, the child stopped screaming, looked up at me and said, *Fuck you*. I wasn't sure what to think, I just started laughing. Then the other women burst out laughing, too. That helped cover the embarrassment.'

Joy also had a lot of people coming in to discuss personal matters. She was older and well known in the community.

A lot of troubled young girls came in to see her. 'Sadly, some had been abused when they were younger and couldn't tell anybody. When I finished at midday, people would leave the clinic, but often a few would hang around to talk to me. Having someone to talk to helped, even though by this stage the damage had been done. The girls didn't want me to do anything – just listen. They'd get it all out and then find it wasn't such a weight after airing whatever had happened to them. Then I'd knock off at 4.30 and people would arrive at the hospital office to talk. I guess I was an unofficial counsellor – someone they could bare their souls to. I got a lot of that. I just had to listen and they'd sort it out themselves from there.'

Professor Donna Mak worked in the Kimberley with Joy for eleven years, from 1989 to 1992 when she was in the Fitzroy Valley, and then from 1995 to 2002, when she was based in Derby as a public health physician for the region. Now the head of Population and Preventive Health at the University of Notre Dame Australia, Donna says in a place where staff turnover was high, with some nurses staying only a few weeks or months, having a long-term community health nurse like Joy was invaluable. 'Joy knew all the patients, in particular the Aboriginal patients and how they were related to each other. She had an excellent working relationship with the Aboriginal health workers and taught me a lot about how to work with Aboriginal people. Not just by being willing to answer my countless questions and share her wisdom and experience with me, but by being an example and a role model. I would watch and listen to see how she did things and try them out for myself. Joy was highly respected by everyone who knew her. She could balance the fine line of being an active member of the local community and keeping the professional distance, when required to be a trusted and confidential health professional. She was extremely hard-working and would put in a full week's work at community health, while looking after her sons, who stayed in town to attend high school. On Friday afternoons she would drive two hours back out to Bulka to work all weekend with Jim on the station. At that stage the house wasn't even built. On Monday morning she would be at community health by 7 am ready to work again.'

After leaving the Kimberley, Donna asked for Joy's help to establish a teaching program, where medical students could live with and work for lay people in remote Australia for a week to learn first-hand about the social determinants of health and develop skills and attitudes required to live out bush. 'Joy's support for the program and participation as a community host from the program's inception in 2006 until she retired from Bulka was instrumental in securing the involvement of pastoralists throughout the West Kimberley. I am very grateful to Joy for all she has taught me and all the smiles, laughs and occasional sad times we shared. I am privileged and blessed to have her as a friend.'

Joy's work in Fitzroy over those years helped pay off the loan for Bulka, and with constant hard work she and Jim developed the property. 'Our first house was a mining donga [a small, transportable building]. We had a gen set put in, a TV and a few basics. Then we got a roof and verandah and bit by bit we built our homestead.'

When Joy turned 60, she was still living in Fitzroy while Jim was at Bulka. 'One morning Jim just said, *I'm getting sick of living on my own, when are you going to give up nursing?* We were still living in this funny old donga, so I said, *When we get a house.*' Almost immediately Jim brought in a portable house and set it up and Joy resigned. 'It was time,' she says. 'We'd built a good cattle herd by then and were making an income on Bulka.'

When Joy looks back now to the late 1960s when she arrived at the Crossing, she realises it was the end of an era. 'We didn't have electricity, telephones, television or air conditioning. The main roads were unsealed. I was there before all that changed. It's not as remote now, and with so many improvements and better roads, tourists can move through the region.'

In 2004 Clinton and John left to work away from home and neither one was interested in taking on the family station. 'It was a big decision, but we decided to sell in 2011.' Joy and Jim moved to a farming district, Badgingarra, and bought some land. They are now 220 kilometres north of Perth, close to the coast – an idyllic spot. 'We still have cattle – about 300 cows – and all Jim has to do is hop on a quad bike for an hour or so and he's seen the whole place. Clinton is a chopper-mustering pilot based out of Broome and is now married. His wife, Rae, flies helicopters, too. We used to say *love is in the air*. John lives and works in Darwin.'

CHAPTER

7

Lisa Peberdy

The sun was setting on the Torres Strait Islands archipelago north of the Cape York Peninsula in Queensland. From the broad, timber verandah at the Thursday Island (TI) Hospital, Lisa Peberdy looked across the shimmering ocean. The seascape was draped in luminous orange light for as far as she could see. On an afternoon shift, the 31-year-old nurse and midwife was taking a breather when a call came in to let her know a woman from Friday Island (located just behind TI) was motoring across in a dinghy with her father and her husband. She had gone into labour at only 36 weeks pregnant.

Lisa grabbed her little delivery pack, a torch, a wheelchair and the wardsman. They rushed down to Bach Beach behind the hospital where the dinghy would stop. They could see a flickering light heading towards them. As the boat drew near Lisa didn't give the resident croc a single thought. She waded in to greet them. The three in the boat looked to her with relief on their faces. 'We had a little chat and I was thankful to see the woman was calm and collected,' Lisa says. 'But suddenly, she gave a bit of a push and a soft groan. I thought, *Oh dear, something is happening here.*' In the quickly fading light, Lisa asked the woman if she minded her having a look. She smiled at Lisa but wasn't really paying attention. 'I lifted her muu-muu and shone the torch to see.' Astonished, Lisa could see the baby's hair presenting. 'It was all on,' she says. 'The delivery pack hadn't been opened – I had no gloves, no nothing. There I was, with my skinny white legs standing knee-deep in the water holding a torch. I turned to the wardsman to ask for some help, but when he realised a baby was coming – and not wanting any part of it – he reversed up the beach, tripping over his own feet. The two men in the boat were of no help, either. They couldn't look or hold the light – this was women's busi-ness and no place for men. It's hard to birth a baby and hold a torch at the same time, so I delivered in the darkness. The mother gave one more push and her baby girl was born.'

Lisa called out to the wardsman to bring down a towel, which he managed to do. As she swathed the baby snugly it sounded out a healthy cry. 'We wheeled them up to the hospital and while we all wished the boat had come in 30 minutes ear-lier, everyone was overjoyed. A lot of midwives say they want a carpark birth – that would be the cream of their career. I think I went one better – a dinghy birth in the Torres Strait.'

Born in Mackay, Queensland in 1968, Lisa moved to the Sunshine Coast with her family when she was in the second grade and attended the Woombye Primary School with her older sister, Leanne, and younger brothers, Grant and Paul. When she completed high school a few of her girlfriends went into nursing and she decided to follow. Enrolled at St Andrew's on Brisbane's Wickham Terrace to train, she met another country girl, Kerry 'Parky' Joseland, who was from a remote cattle property in western Queensland. 'We became close, lifelong friends. At seventeen and with fun high on the agenda, Parky and I were ratbags on a roll.'

The day after Lisa graduated, her fifteen-year-old brother, Paul, with whom she was very close, went missing in the surf. 'Paul was a surf lifesaving nipper and had been training at the Alexandra Headland Surf Life Saving Club for an upcoming surf carnival,' Lisa recalls.

The well-known Ironman and surf lifesaver Grant Kenny was also a member of the surf club and that was the weekend he married Olympian swimmer Lisa Curry. The senior lifesavers were away for the wedding, leaving just the teenagers on the beach that day. 'It was fairly rough and Paul was knocked off his board three times – the third time he didn't resurface. It was presumed he was knocked unconscious and killed.' Lisa's family endured a three-day search before finding Paul's body. The tragedy was the catalyst that made Lisa realise how precious life was and the importance of getting out and living life to the full.

She stayed on the Sunshine Coast after Paul's death, working at the Nambour Selangor Private Hospital as an enrolled nurse. Later she travelled extensively overseas for almost a year. On her return, encouraged by friend and fellow nurse Kerry Joseland, she found a bush placement in the small town of Barcaldine, in central west Queensland. Kerry was nursing at Blackall, 107 kilometres south of Barcaldine.

Lisa really enjoyed the little community and the diversity of a country hospital. It was a huge change as she had never been that far west before. Barcaldine is 1080 kilometres north-west of Brisbane in Queensland's central west. The major industries are sheep and beef cattle production. Barcaldine is famous for its role in the development of the Australian Labour Party after the shearer's strike of 1891. Today it's a laidback rural town of 1700 people with a lot of pubs, cattle and sheep producers and a plethora of unusual buildings.

There were a few beds for maternity up one end of the building and some for aged care. 'I was a general nurse and would run a mile if I heard someone was in labour. That end of the hospital was very scary. That was for the midwives and they could have it – I'd take on anything else. I was there for about twelve months and learned a great deal. It was also my first real contact with Indigenous health work.

'Kerry and I went to every possible bachelor and spinster [B&S] ball, and despite having to drive long distances over unsealed roads to get anywhere, we led a very busy social life. Sometimes Kerry and I would head off to her family's property near the tiny outback town of Yaraka. Once we went out there in Kerry's little white Gemini and while we were out there it rained. We both had to get back to work and although we were told not to drive because of dangerous wet dirt-road conditions, we headed off in the Gemini. We spent most of the time sliding sideways or spinning – it took us hours, but we got there. The car was coated in red mud; there wasn't a speck of white on it by the time we hit the bitumen road.'

At 21, Lisa thought her career options were limited as an enrolled nurse. To build on her one-year course, she returned to Nambour to repeat Year 12 as a mature-age student and then enrolled for a three-year nursing degree at the Queensland University of Technology (QUT) in Brisbane and graduated with distinction. She completed her graduate year at the Nambour General Hospital in 1995, which is where she met Min Lene, who took a group of students to Samoa to complete their prac by doing postnatal visits in a community. It was her first exposure to midwifery.

'On the islands resources are limited and Lisa would go out of her way to compromise and find ways around problems,' Min says. 'Later when she was in Sydney doing her midwifery, she rang me. She had gone out to visit a Samoan family with a senior midwife. When they walked into the house there was food on the table and the family invited them to eat. The midwife was standoffish in terms of engagement and told Lisa not to eat anything. They were there for a postnatal check.

'Lisa sat down regardless to have a cup of tea and a bite to eat with the family. She knew the offering of food was special and culturally significant – like shaking a hand. She had learned how to engage and to form a trusting relationship. I suggested she go back to her teacher and recommend a session in multicultural communication.'

During her time at university, Lisa met and dated Pete. After her year at Nambour, Pete was transferred to Sydney for his work. She was determined to go with him. With an oversupply of nurses in the mid-1990s, Lisa couldn't find a job as a general nurse in Sydney. Her only option was to apply for a midwifery course. 'My friends and family fell about laughing,' she says. 'They all knew I couldn't watch a birth on film, let alone help deliver a baby. As far as I was concerned, childbirth was the worst thing in the world. I had only really been involved in postnatal care in Samoa.'

She was accepted into the University of Western Sydney and studied two days a week for the theory component and was employed three days at the Nepean Hospital.

'I was excited to be there, but lo and behold on my first rotation roster I was assigned to the labour ward for a straight month,' she says. The first time Lisa attended the birth of a baby and saw the placenta discharge from the mother's womb, that was it – she vomited! 'There I was, training to be a midwife,' she says. 'Everybody said *Get out now, Peberdy, you're never going to make it.*

'We were the very first uni students to come through university training and the midwives didn't agree with the change from hospital-based training,' Lisa says. 'But there was a midwife, Anne, of whom everyone – even the experienced midwives – was a bit afraid. But it was Anne who got me through. I was the country girl living away from home in the city and she felt sorry for me. She took me under her wing and that's how I made it through that first month.'

The last four weeks of the course, and Lisa's last hurdle, was in the labour ward. In the third week, she experienced the birth of a stillborn baby. 'It was very, very traumatic,' she says. 'I cried and cried. I honestly thought, *That's it, this is not for me, I am out of here.*'

The senior midwives stepped in. They walked and talked her through the experience and convinced her not to throw away her hard work.

No longer going out with Pete, who had been transferred to Melbourne, and concerned she might never leave Sydney if she didn't make a break, Lisa decided to take a placement at Kalgoorlie, which had a strong graduate midwifery program for twelve months. The program was established to encourage midwives to go there because it was hard to recruit staff to Kalgoorlie. 'I returned to the coast for a brief holiday after finishing my midwifery training. I left for Kalgoorlie from the Sunshine Coast in my Mazda 121 bubble car with my girlfriend Lorrine in 1996. We drove all the way to Kalgoorlie. We laughed our way across the Nullarbor Plain and the flat, treeless, arid country of southern Australia. We were two girls with a tiny bubble car packed to the roof with all our worldly belongings, including a bike rack on the back with two push-bikes and a little tent so we could camp along the way to Kalgoorlie. We attracted a lot of comments – the most common being that our pushbikes were our spares.'

It was in Kalgoorlie that Lisa finally overcame her fear of the labour ward. 'I was working in a small unit and had to work in all areas of midwifery, including the birth suite and ward. I was a slow starter, but I did come to love the labour ward. When you train to birth a baby, the first three times you double-scrub with a senior midwife – which means you place your hands over hers to feel the movement and learn how to guide the baby through the birth canal. You birth the baby together.'

But Lisa was still feeling frightened by the birthing experience after three double-scrubs. She double-scrubbed up to fifteen times. Every time the birth drew close, instead of handling the birth on her own, she'd ask the senior midwife on duty to double-scrub. 'Before long I was asked how many double-scrubs I'd done. Word had got out. Then one day when I put my gloves on for another imminent birth and called on the midwife who had done the last five births with me to double-scrub, she said no problem.

'*Quick*, I called fretfully, *I need your hands.*

'*No you don't.*

'*Yes I do!*

'*Look*, she said, *you're doing it on your own.* I just had to keep going with her encouraging me all the way. I was terrified throughout the birth, but once the baby arrived, it was exhilarating. I had done it on my own and it was a fantastic feeling.' The training wheels were off and after that Lisa couldn't do enough time in the labour ward. 'To think I originally had no desire or intention to become a midwife, then bang – I was hooked.'

Not long after, Lisa observed a birth of another stillborn baby. A young couple who were in town to work in the goldmine had made friends with Lisa. Like her they were from Queensland. 'I had been caring for the woman and the couple was excited about the pending birth of their first child,' Lisa says. 'They came in when the baby hadn't moved for a while. We monitored and discovered the baby had died. It was even harder when the young woman had to come back in the next day for an induction. It was a very long labour with a large baby that had to be birthed naturally. They gave the baby the same name as the baby that had died in my midwifery course the year before. It was extremely traumatic and sad. It was the worst of midwifery. You have the best of it when everything goes well and a beautiful healthy baby is born, then you have times like that. You grieve with the parents, push through the sad times and you just have to move on. Another baby comes with another wonderful experience and your faith and strength is restored.'

In Kalgoorlie, Lisa was introduced to the Hay Street sex workers. 'We did all the screening and sexually transmissible infections checks,' she says. 'I did a community placement and I found the work really interesting. The women were straight-forward, smart and funny. There were schoolteachers, secretaries and mothers. They came to Kalgoorlie for short periods of time to earn some extra money. I was still in my early twenties and found it a huge eye-opener.'

Over a year in Kalgoorlie, Lisa learned a great deal about midwifery and Indigenous health. 'It was a great hands-off birthing environment and with high-risk pregnant women sent to Perth, the majority of births were natural and uncomplicated. It was a lovely place to learn midwifery.'

Looking for a new adventure, Lisa left Kalgoorlie in late 1997 to work in Darwin. 'I was still in contact and friends with Pete. He flew into Perth and we headed off to Darwin.'

Once there, Lisa took a job in maternity at the Royal Darwin Hospital. 'I loved working there and stayed for twelve months. There were about six of us young midwives who had chosen the Territory for the experience. Most of the work involved Indigenous health with women coming in from all over the Top End from remote communities. English was not their first language and they were the sweetest yet strongest women I'd ever met. They could be quite cheeky so we had some fun times, lots of laughs and it was such a pleasure to work with them. They'd birth beautifully with no breastfeeding problems – no mastitis, cracked nipples or poor milk supply. They'd just put the babies on the boob and off they'd go. When the women are in labour, you know they're getting close to birthing when a little sweat appears on the mother's brow. That's how good the women are. They don't show pain – just extraordinary strength and resolve.'

Lisa cared for an Indigenous woman from Elcho Island, which is off the coast of Arnhem Land at the southern end of the Wessel Islands group. 'Jacqueline was brought to Darwin in premature labour at around 34 weeks. Lisa birthed her little boy, David, and cared for him for about six weeks before he was big enough to go home. Years later when I returned to Gove as the Women's Health educator, Jacqueline and I recognised each other in the clinic on Elcho Island one day. She brought David into the clinic so I could see him. I couldn't believe how big he had grown. Born a tiny premie, I assumed he would still be small for his age, but he was actually quite tall and very solid. It was wonderful to see him so well as I had often wondered how he was going after he left hospital. You form a close attachment to the babies that stay with you for a long period. David had no idea who I was of course and he was quite perplexed about all the fuss that day.'

At the end of her twelve months in Darwin and keen to return to Queensland, Lisa got a job on Thursday Island. It was at the end of 1998. With a population of 2610, TI is the administrative centre for the Australian islands between Cape York and the New Guinea mainland. It sits in the Prince of Wales Island group, or the Inner Islands, and is 35 kilometres north-west of Australia's northern extremity, Cape York.

'I wanted to go to TI because I was really enjoying working in Indigenous health. It was so much more interesting.' She arrived to a very small midwifery unit in a 30-bed hospital with six maternity beds and two birthing rooms. The midwifery section was built over the water. 'Sitting on the verandah with women from the Torres Strait Islands and Papua New Guinea is a memory I'll carry forever. On quieter days, with the sound of water lapping under us on high tide, we'd yarn and laugh away. After giving birth, the mothers would be starving. I'd grab them a meal with dessert from the kitchen. There were lounge chairs all the way down one wall of the ward and the women, to be close to the midwives, loved to sit on those chairs and natter away and give the midwives a bit of cheek, too. I'd sit down next to them and grab any spare meals I could find – my excuse was that we'd both worked hard birthing the baby!'

The heat and humidity were oppressive, but Lisa got used to it. 'Bad hair days and sweating were the norm for me.' She laughs. 'To get to the hospital we'd run a hundred metres from the air-conditioned nurses' quarters to the air-conditioned hospital as fast as we could. We had to cross the road that circumnavigated the island – TI's only major road. The island is three kilometres by three kilometres. The hospital was built three years before I arrived. Nurses had their own double bedroom and en suite and shared a kitchen between four rooms and a lounge room between eight rooms. It was a whole lot of fun. Male and female nurses were there from all over Australia.'

The Torres Strait Island–trained health workers worked alongside the midwives in the hospital's maternity ward. 'There was nothing we could do that they couldn't,' Lisa says. 'They were fantastic. One in particular, Margie, was incredible. She'd go in and take care of the women and she'd be in there doing all the work. If you had an emergency, you'd want Margie beside you. A lot of the women had eight or more children, increasing the risk of postpartum haemorrhage (PPH).'

Some women bleed too much after birth and require special treatment. It occurs in up to six per cent of births and is most likely to happen while the placenta is separating or soon after. 'There was also a lot of shoulder dystocia, which can happen during the end of the second stage of labour,' Lisa adds. 'A lot of the babies were very big and would get stuck.' Shoulder dystocia is a case of obstructed labour, where after the delivery of the baby's head, the anterior shoulder can't pass through or requires significant manipulation to pass. It's diagnosed when the shoulders fail to deliver shortly after the head and can be an obstetric emergency. 'Sometimes you have to break the clavicle [collarbone] to get the baby out or it might just be a matter of manoeuvring women, having them change position to allow their pelvis to open as wide as possible. Margie was unbelievable with all of that.'

The Queensland health department flew the nursing staff as far as Cairns every six months for a well-earned break. 'There was one grocery store, a post office, newsagent, a clothing store called Mona's Bazaar and a couple of takeaways and three pubs. So it was a big thing to get home to the coast for a good shop and to see family. I flew home as often as I could. I made some great friends on TI and we still keep in contact today.'

At TI Lisa was assigned to regular night duty. She was keen to get back to working the Monday-to-Friday, nine-to-five shift so she could go camping on weekends. While the outreach midwife was on long-service leave, Lisa relieved in her position for a couple of months. 'This meant flying out to a different island every day to do the antenatal and postnatal care in midwifery clinics on the outer islands. We'd fly off in a helicopter or small fixed-wing plane. It was exciting to be flying to work every day in such an extraordinary place. It was Monday to Friday and I loved it. I got to see all the outer islands.'

When the position of sexual health nurse became available Lisa put her hand up. She had learned a lot about sexual health in Kalgoorlie and how to do a pap smear while in Darwin. She got the job and began the rounds on the outer islands, carrying out sexual health screening. But it had been a long time since she had cared for 'grown-up' male patients. 'I was doing both boys and girls, so this was another eye-opener for me. I'd trained in sexual and reproductive health with Family Planning in Darwin, so I just had to put the training to practice.'

On her first day in the job as sexual health nurse, a boatload of illegal fishermen from Indonesia had been caught in the Torres Strait and brought in for health checks. 'I got a call from the receptionist at the clinic saying there were some patients for Thomas and me. Thomas, the health worker, had gone off to lunch. *Oh, I'll be right down*, I said, hoping she wouldn't detect my extreme nervousness. I walked in to find about ten men and the quarantine officer – all dark, all non-English speaking and all with huge smiles on their faces.'

Anxiously, Lisa wondered how she would deal with them. 'I hadn't dealt with men for so long,' she says. 'Thomas was off on a break on island time and didn't surface for quite a while. Island time is slow and relaxed – clock time is unobserved. Eventually, he wandered back in and we ended up staying late that night to process the men. We did full screens and took blood and found they all had infections. I'd never seen anything like it. Thomas was very experienced and led the way for me. After that the men, who were staying on Horn Island in the quarantine area, came back to the clinic once or twice a week for a jab of penicillin. They named me Dr Love. I'd walk into the waiting room be greeted by big wide grins and a chorusing of *Dr Loooooovvve*. They were always smiling and laughing and I soon discovered, very sweet.'

While Lisa was on TI, she answered a call for midwives to work in East Timor in the wake of the humanitarian and security crisis of 1999 to 2000. Lisa took three months' leave without pay from TI in 2000. One of six Australian volunteers – five midwives and one retired doctor – she joined the International Medical Corps, an American-founded aid organisation.

Her work was based in Oecusse Enclave, where 45,000 refugees were displaced in camps. Because of the geographical isolation from the rest of East Timor, this was where the worst of the atrocities had occurred. 'We provided clinical support and education to local health staff and were on call 24 hours a day, six days a week for obstetric and general emergencies at the district hospital. We also ran mobile clinics to remote villages in the hills under armed guard from the Jordanian and Australian armies, as there were still rogue West Timor soldiers. We also developed education programs for midwifery care, women's health, sexual health and child health.'

Volunteers lived and worked under extreme circumstances with a moderate to high security risk. There was no electricity, running water or diagnostic or screening equipment; there were limited pharmaceuticals, they were isolated from support military units and there was an extreme language barrier.

Back on TI, when the position of mobile women's health nurse came up in Mount Isa, Lisa applied. Still in the area of sexual health, she wanted to get back into women's health. 'I had no desire to go to Mount Isa. I was aware it was hot, dry, ugly and in the middle of nowhere. My preference was a coastal position in Cairns, or perhaps Townsville – somewhere nice. But lo and behold, I got the Mount Isa job. I had only really interviewed for the experience, and despite getting the job, I had no intention of taking it.' But every time Lisa called to decline, Matron Beth Anderson was on the other end of the phone. She had established the position and been in the job for ten years and she had been matron of the hospital for more than twenty years before that. 'I kept trying to say I wasn't interested, but each time Beth would talk me out of it. You soon learned you just didn't say no to Miss Anderson. I had got myself into this predicament and the next thing I knew I was heading to Mount Isa.'

It meant leaving the Torres Strait before she was ready. Every day for the first month in Mount Isa Lisa cried. 'It was worse than I'd imagined. Brown, dusty, full of flies and there was no water to swim in. I moved in December 2001 and every day the mercury was pushing 40 degrees. I hated it. I kept thinking, *What have I done?*'

Lisa stayed in Mount Isa for three years and after that first harrowing month, began to love it. Her job was to run the women's health clinic in Queensland's Gulf region. 'We flew or drove to wonderful small towns, including Cloncurry,

Burketown, Normanton, Karumba, Camooweal, Doomadgee, Julia Creek and Mornington Island. Under the Rural and Remote Women's Health program we ran clinics in remote places in conjunction with the Royal Flying Doctor Service [RFDS]. The RFDS has several different programs – the emergency retrieval service, primary health clinics and women's health clinics. The Queensland Health Mobile Women's Health Service worked in partnership with the RFDS Rural and Remote Women's Health Program and Queensland Health part funded the RFDS program.

'I grew to absolutely love the country I was working and the work itself. I lived in a little house next to the hospital, which was in turn next door to the units where all the young doctors lived. On weekends the other nurses and I would go out with them. There was a whole new bunch of people to get to know. Some I had already met in Darwin or the Torres Strait. When you work in rural and remote you often see the same people. The same group tends to move around the posts. I was really drawn to that lifestyle.'

Lisa travelled to outreach health clinics in a LandCruiser, mostly on her own. One day on her return to Mount Isa from Normanton, her vehicle was packed to the hilt with clinic and lab gear, a folding bed, speculums (the 'duck bill' tool used for pap smears) and more. 'It was late afternoon and I had just driven past the Cloncurry turn-off when I heard, *hiss, hiss, hiss* followed by a loud bang. A blowout. I pulled to the side of the road and took a look.' There was very little left of the tyre. Lisa knew she had to change it on her own. 'I thought, *I'm too far from anyone to call for help.* I had to unload the back of the vehicle and lay all the gear on the side of road. Then I tried to jack the car up. But I couldn't raise it high enough to take the blown tyre off and put a new one on.' The ground was rock hard. She decided to dig a little trench to make it easier. The sticks she gathered were too weak; then she remembered she had some metal speculums left over from the clinic. She could use one of them like a shovel. She got the largest one out and started digging. After 45 minutes and getting quite tired, she could hear a vehicle approaching. 'I thought, *This could be good or bad. I'm in the middle of nowhere.*'

To her relief it was a Queensland Health four-wheel drive full of medical students and an intern. 'I recognised them from around the hospital. *You're in a spot of trouble,* they said. I was standing there covered in dust and holding a dirty metal speculum. *We'll give you a hand.* So I passed the speculum to one of them and said *I still have six more in the car.* I handed them all one and saved the smallest one for me to make sure I did the least amount of work from this point in. There we were all armed with a speculum. We dug the trench and changed the tyre. We couldn't stop laughing as we were working. The boys were coming up with 101 uses for the metal speculum.' The Mount Isa paper heard about that day and wrote about the women's health nurse who used a metal speculum to change a tyre.

At the same time Lisa was in Mount Isa, Vivienne Manesis worked as a general practitioner for the Aboriginal and Islander Health Service based in Townsville and regularly flew to Mount Isa and then into remote communities for Rural Women's Health clinics funded by the RFDS.

One day Vivienne and Lisa were flown by charter flight to Mornington Island to run a clinic. 'It was only the second time we'd met,' Vivienne says. 'It was the wet season and we ran into a storm during the flight. It came up suddenly and the pilot couldn't get above or below it. I suffer from motion sickness, so I was feeling physically unwell and was about to vomit in the sick bag. There was an Aboriginal health worker on board who neither of us really knew. She was on the exit window and looking as though she was about to open the exit door and jump out. Lisa just kept talking and talking and talking. When you feel sick and anxious like I was, and this person was yak, yak, yak the whole time, it's not good. Apparently I told her to shut up. And she basically said, *Nah, if I'm going to die, I'm going to die talking.* She was obviously anxious, too, and that was her way of getting through the flight. When you land on Mornington Island the first thing you see is a memorial for eight people who did lose their lives in an air crash. I said to the pilot, *If that storm's still there this afternoon we're not getting back on the plane.* He was a very good pilot though, and he got us there and back safely.' As a result of the storm, Lisa said it was at that point when they were returning to Mount Isa that she considered launching her open-ocean-swimming career to get back to safe dry land – crocs or no crocs in the water.

Lisa also spent time on the Gove Peninsula as a women's health educator, which was the next level up for her. Gove is on the west coast of the Gulf of Carpentaria within Arnhem Land and includes the towns of Nhulunbuy, Alyangula on Groote Eylandt, the islands of Galiwin'ku and Milingimbi and the major Aboriginal communities on the main land. It's a vast tract of Aboriginal title land on the Northern Territory coastline. The little township of Nhulunbuy is the main commercial and service centre of the Peninsula and lies 600 kilometres east of Darwin.

The hospital is a 32-bed acute-care facility and fifteen remote community clinics refer patients to the hospital for inpatient, outpatient and specialist care. Sitting just twelve degrees south of the equator, the Gove Peninsula has a monsoon climate.

Two distinct seasons are recognised as the dry season from May to October and the wet from November to April. During the dry season there is virtually no rainfall, clear blue skies and cool ocean breezes. The wet season brings the monsoon weather with hot and humid days and warm nights. Electrical storms are spectacular and cyclonic activity is not uncommon in the wet season. The majority of transport is by aircraft.

The time came when Lisa thought she was ready to head home. 'When I was based in Mount Isa, I was one of thirteen mobile women's health nurses employed throughout rural and remote Queensland and we were coordinated centrally through Queensland Health's Cancer Screening Services unit in Brisbane. When the position of coordinator for those nurses came up, I applied and got it. Once again, I wasn't expecting it – I just threw my hat in the ring. That's how I came back to Brisbane in 2005.' Lisa enjoyed working there until October 2012, when the Newman state government suddenly made 15,000 public-servant positions redundant. She was working in cancer-screening services at the time as the Nursing Director, Cervical Cancer Screening. The government felt it was too top heavy and too costly to continue, so disbanded the cancer-screening coordination unit, along with many other specialist units.

Not wanting to go back to shift work, Lisa applied for a position with Cell Care, Australia's largest private cord-blood-bank company based in Melbourne. Now, at 47, Lisa is the state manager in Queensland. She has also undertaken a PhD looking into cord-blood stem-cell therapy, and patients', obstetricians' and midwives' understanding of it. She's focusing on cell volume, cord clamping time and health professionals' knowledge of stem cells and placental transfusion. It's a new and exciting area in Australia. 'Umbilical cord blood and tissue are rich in powerful stem cells that can only be collected at birth for potential future use,' Lisa says. 'Stem cells have the ability to create and regenerate the organs, blood, tissue and immune system that make up our bodies. There's only one chance to collect and store a baby's cord blood and tissue stem cells and that's at birth.' A trained Cell Care collector, obstetrician or midwife performs the cell collection process, which is quick and painless for both mother and baby.

Late one afternoon Lisa received a call from an obstetrician asking if she had a spare cord-blood collection kit. She was just about to take a woman with a baby in trouble to theatre at Brisbane's Wesley Hospital and wanted to collect the cord blood. Lisa told her she was fifteen minutes away. 'My phone rang when I got in the car and the woman asked if I had two kits. There were twins and they wanted to collect from both to help the baby in trouble. I ran back upstairs and got the second kit. But on the way I got held up in peak-hour traffic. The receptionist rang: *Where are you? They're in theatre and they're waiting for the kits.*

'*I'm stuck in the traffic,* I told her. *Can you ask them to leave the cord clamps on the cords and I'll get there as soon as I can.* The traffic was moving slowly. I told her I was three sets of lights away and asked if she could meet me at the front door and take my car away – no time to find a park. When I arrived I jumped out of the car, grabbed the kits and rushed into the theatre. *I'm here to do cord-blood collection on the twins,* I said.'

Lisa changed, scrubbed and rushed in. The obstetrician looked up at her.

'*Thank God you're here,*' was her welcome.

'*Where are the placentas?*' Lisa asked.

'*Still inside the uterus.*'

'What time were the babies born?'
'Twenty-five minutes ago.'

'Usually, after this amount of time the placentas have been delivered and I collect the blood afterwards,' Lisa says. 'The obstetrician said, *Well, Lisa you've always told me the best collections are the ones you collect when the placenta is still inside. So I held them there for you.*

'That's never happened in a caesarian situation before,' Lisa says. 'The doctor had kept the uterus open with the placentas attached waiting for the cord blood to be collected. It was quite a big thing and an exciting time. It all went well for the two little boys and we collected good blood volumes.'

Most people think once the baby is born the cord is clamped immediately in order to collect the cord blood for storage, but Lisa says that's not so. 'In order to collect an adequate volume of cells as well as allowing the baby to get as much blood as possible, we need to clamp the cord at one minute post-birth. By this stage the baby has already received approximately 75 percent of the blood that was left in the placenta. Then we collect the remaining amount.'

The baby or the family can use the cells if needed later in life. The newborn's umbilical cord stem cells are a perfect match for the child and, more than likely, any siblings and family members. That's why it's known as family cord banking.

Never did Lisa think she'd end up working in Brisbane again. 'I often talk to nursing and midwifery students about the possibilities after graduation and tell them working in rural and remote areas is the best experience personally and professionally. You can't beat it. You meet some great characters along the way and you learn to appreciate the important things in life. When city people I know get stressed about small issues,

I usually say to them, *Did someone die as a result? No? Well that's not a drama, sit down and let me tell you a story.*'

But Lisa's life now is back in the city. Five years ago, at 42, she met Mark Fairbairne. 'I never planned not to marry. I was just used to being on my own and able to do what I wanted, when I wanted. But when I met this lovely man, a Kiwi, everything changed.' He is the manager of Queensland's largest drug and alcohol centre in Brisbane – so he's also a health worker. 'He's very urbane with little outback experience,' Lisa says with a laugh. They married five years ago and Lisa is now the proud stepmother of Dea.

CHAPTER

8

Wendy Agars

It was three in the morning when the Northern Territory Aerial Medical Service (NTAMS) pilot made an instrument approach into a remote community in the Gulf of Carpentaria, Northern Territory. With poor visibility due to low cloud and lack of moonlight, he set the aircraft down on what's known as a 'black hole' night. It was the mid-1990s during the wet season, and midwife Wendy Agars was on board, tasked to pick up a man with a respiratory problem.

As Wendy emerged from the plane the heady mix of kerosene, aviation fuel and dust was hard-hitting. In the distance, a vehicle's beaming headlights ignited the black night. Wendy trod carefully towards the light until she could see a troopy packed with people. A pregnant woman was sitting in the front seat between the remote-area nurse and a locum doctor. The patient with the respiratory problem was in the back seat with members of his family. The sound of low, hushed voices suggested quite a few women were waiting in another vehicle nearby.

The nurse asked Wendy if she could fly out the pregnant woman as well as the man she had flown in for. There hadn't been time for a proper examination, but she was concerned that at an estimated 35 weeks pregnant, the woman might have a urinary tract infection. Wendy worried it may not be safe to take her on the plane in a nurse-only situation. 'There hadn't been any consultation with the medical officer [MO] or acceptance at the hospital,' Wendy says. 'I wondered whether both patients were stable. I thought, *Maybe a doctor is needed? We'll have to go back to the clinic and call the MO to decide.*'

She leaned into the vehicle to greet both patients and check their condition. She knew she'd have to find out exactly what was happening with the pregnant woman. She made a mental checklist: Is she contracting? Is she sure of her dates? Has she ruptured her membranes? What number baby is this for her? Has there been a premature birth before? 'I needed to examine her to see if she was dilating and find out if the baby was cephalic [head first] and find out how low in the pelvis the baby was. I knew I'd have to establish all this and more before we made the decision to evacuate her. The golden rule is if a baby is close to being born and there's a risk of an inflight birth, then stay put. Go back to the clinic where the environment is safer.'

Wendy took a closer look. The woman was sitting quietly and still. Wendy could see she was frightened. 'I noticed a few beads of sweat on her nose and I thought, *Uh-oh something is going on with you.* Then suddenly she gave a big, involuntary push. And with that, all hell broke loose. The men in the troopy realised a birth was imminent and with lightning speed scrambled out and took flight.'

In low light Wendy and the doctor carefully helped the woman to lie along the front seat. Her mother cradled her head from the driver's side and comforted her. 'Then the expectant mum called out, *The baby is coming*,' Wendy says. 'I removed her undergarments and to our surprise and alarm we could see a tiny foot, followed by another. I thought, *Oh my God, here we are in this very remote location, in the dead of night on the side of an airstrip with a patient I wasn't expecting. She's about to give birth, the baby is breech and there's not enough time to get back to the health centre.*' Wendy clicked into overdrive. She asked the pilot to grab the delivery pack from the plane. He had done some ambulance work in the past and it was showing. He raced back to the plane and grabbed further oxygen and a spare suction unit, the drug box and bunny rugs. 'He was an amazing assistant and I thought, *Yep, you've been in situations like this before.*'

The expectant mother's women relatives were chatting excitedly and ready to pitch in. The troopy was running to keep the internal light and her grandmother resourcefully warmed the bunny rug and towels by draping them on the warm bonnet. The bewildered locum doctor had only just arrived from Sydney and the bush experience was brand new. 'I felt for him,' says Wendy. 'He was only in the community for three weeks and hadn't seen an aeromedical evacuation. He really only came down to the airstrip out of curiosity. He stood near the passenger's door ready to assist in the birth.' With trembling hands, Wendy set up the oxygen, suction, and bag valve mask and drew up an injection of Syntocinon. 'Here we were delivering a baby with barely any light, very few resources and no back-up.'

Despite the breech presentation, the labour process was smooth and steady with the cervix dilating for the baby to descend. 'There can be a lot of concern around birthing a breech baby, but I've seen quite a few and I hoped this birth would not be a problem despite our less-than-ideal location,' Wendy says. 'I remembered the other golden rule – *hands off the breech*. I thought, *Please let her be fully dilated so the head isn't trapped*. We needed to keep the baby warm, to wait until the nape of the neck and the hairline were visible before doing any manoeuvring – if at all. If we had to touch the baby, we needed to handle it gently by the pelvic girdle, not around its little abdomen, to avoid injury.' Wendy's primary focus was to assist the mum to breathe out the baby's head – gently and slowly.

'As the baby emerged I was putting my two bobs' worth in to the doctor about safely birthing a breech,' Wendy says, laughing. 'I wasn't sure he had done one before. I hovered behind him and the nurse, peeping in between their waists to see what was happening. I knew things could go awfully wrong and if they did, we would all have to deal with the situation at hand using the resources we had.'

Everyone had a job to do and they worked together. Thankfully, the baby's arms and shoulders emerged without too much handling and then her head appeared. 'To our delight she gave a hearty cry. We placed her on her mum's tummy and cleaned her with the towel. I don't think there was a dry eye among us.'

Everyone's joy was palpable. Wendy could see the big relief and thrill on the faces of the grandmother, aunty and mother. 'Aunty cut the cord and the nurse gave the mum some Syntocinon to help deliver the placenta. It came away uneventfully and without excessive bleeding. We inserted an IV cannula just in case, but everything went really well. This night strengthened my faith that leaving things well enough alone is often the best.'

With the mother's bleeding settled, Wendy's thoughts turned to the original patient she had come to collect. She shone her Dolphin torch over by the plane and there he was, propped against the aircraft wheel. 'He didn't want to be near the women's business either,' Wendy says. 'So the other men had picked him up and moved him. They had seated him upright to make his breathing easier and his family was looking after him. The pilot and I loaded him onto the aircraft stretcher and made our way back to our base hospital.' The mother and baby were taken back to the health centre for further stabilisation. It was safer for the two to stay in the clinic overnight rather than flying on a plane so soon after the birth. The day crew flew in the next morning to retrieve them. 'It was lovely to catch up with the mother and baby in the hospital the next day and to talk over the amazing birth,' Wendy says.

Born in Adelaide in 1961, Wendy began her university-based nursing training at the Sturt College of Advanced Education straight from school in 1979 and finished in 1981. She had done well on the maternity module and thought she would carry on with what she enjoyed and came easily. 'I knew midwifery would broaden my career opportunities,' she says. Wendy had heard Scotland was a well-thought-of place to train. It sounded exciting, so in 1984 at 23 years of age she left home and flew to Edinburgh. 'As soon as the Qantas jumbo was hurtling along the runway, I thought, *Oh my God what am I getting into? I'm leaving family, friends and home.*' But this decision marked the beginning of Wendy's interminable sense of adventure, desire to travel and extraordinary midwifery career.

In Edinburgh Wendy lived in the Florence Nightingale nurses' home. One of walls had a brick that was from Florence's original home. 'It was very old-fashioned training, but a great place to learn,' Wendy says.

Wendy loved community placement during her training. The midwives zipped around the streets of Edinburgh in little Mini Minors – the home-visiting cars of the community-midwife fleet. They wore a cape and beret and carried their gear in little suitcases. 'We used Pinard stethoscopes [a little wooden tool used by midwives to listen to heart rates] – there was no such thing as a Doppler foetal heart monitor back then,' Wendy says. 'I attended a couple of homebirths during that time and I just knew midwifery was for me.'

There were about a dozen midwives in training with Wendy – girls from around the world. 'Our bedrooms in the quarters were small with great big baths and the bathrooms had heated towel rails – totally foreign to me. Sometimes our food went missing from the shared kitchen so we decided to start hanging it in bags out on the window ledge to keep an eye on it. But it would often freeze overnight. A stop was put to that to protect the pedestrians below.'

After graduation and with only a week left on her visa, Wendy had to leave the United Kingdom. 'I travelled around Europe and the Greek islands and Ireland with another mid-wife and then after eight months, I felt homesick.' She returned to Adelaide, but before long she was keen to travel again. 'I applied to hospitals in Darwin and New Zealand for work and they suggested I gain my postgraduate certificate in midwifery first. So I did that at Flinders Medical Centre and it was indeed a great experience and year of confidence building.'

On landing a job at Royal Darwin Hospital, Wendy arrived in the Northern Territory with very little idea of what lay ahead. Until then she hadn't thought for one minute she would work in the bush – but she was ready. 'It was 1988 and Darwin was a wild old place at that time,' she says. 'But the minute I stepped off the plane onto that shimmering tarmac and into the heat, I thought, *This isn't the dry and dusty frontier I thought it was.* It was lush, green and tropical, with a lingering scent of frangipanis in the air and countless palm trees. I loved it instantly. I asked the taxi driver how best to cope with the heat and humidity and he said, *Let it be mind over matter.* I've heeded his advice ever since.'

When Wendy called in to the Darwin Hospital's nursing office to hand in her paperwork, she was shocked to be greeted by a barefooted staff member wearing jeans and a T-shirt. It was clear life in the Territory was going to be very laidback. 'And little did I know, it would be my home for the next eighteen years,' she says.

At the hospital Wendy experienced her first contact with Indigenous women and embraced the opportunity to learn all she could about Aboriginal culture and a different way of life. 'My plan was to work in midwifery in Darwin for twelve months and then decide where next,' she says. 'But before the end of the year there was a call for midwives to work in Nhulunbuy, a town on the Gove Peninsula, East Arnhem Land.' Nhulunbuy was established in the late sixties with a bauxite mine and deep-water port nearby. The 4000-strong population included predominantly traditional owners (the Yolgnu people), miners and people working in support services to the mine.

A whole new world opened up. 'I was very green and had a lot to learn,' Wendy admits. 'It was a 30-bed hospital with a ten-bed, low-risk maternity unit that also served surrounding communities. On any given maternity shift there was one midwife and a mothercraft nurse. Women came in for sit-down at 36 weeks, leaving behind their family and often other children, which was very difficult for them. Looking after both Indigenous and non-Indigenous women in a low-risk unit broadened my perspective as a midwife in so many ways. I soaked up skills from other incredibly passionate and knowledgeable midwives,' she says. 'I learned the value of active labour and became more attuned to the nuances of when things were going okay to when they started to veer from the course of normal. I learned when to intervene and call for medical help and when to sit on my hands. I learned about normal labour and how to keep it that way and to have faith in women's ability to birth their babies with minimal intervention. And essentially, I learned to trust my own instincts.'

Women from the community of Yirrkala came into Nhulunbuy in large groups to help their young women in labour. They surrounded them with love and stroked their bellies, encouraging the babies to come. The pregnant women usually preferred to be in a room together and after the birth of their babies they would often be found outside contentedly breastfeeding under shady trees in the hospital grounds.

Wendy's friend and nursing colleague Roxy Dale recalls her time at Nhulunbuy with Wendy. 'She was a beautiful and caring midwife,' Roxy says. 'If any of the nurses at the hospital were pregnant they wanted Wendy as their midwife – and she helped birth quite a few of their babies,' she says.

Wendy stayed at Nhulunbuy for eighteen months before heading down the coast to Numbulwar, a community with around 600 people on the Gulf of Carpentaria. Someone was needed to relieve a nurse for three months. 'I very gingerly put my hand up for the job because I didn't have a big background in emergency nursing or in Indigenous health – apart from midwifery. But I'd heard great things about remote-area nursing – so off I went.' There were no telephones and all outside communication was by radio. Wendy's contact person for patient consultations was the doctor on Groote Eylandt. He came in to Numbulwar once a week to conduct a clinic with the assistance of the NTAMS nurses and allied health staff from Nhulunbuy.

Wendy had quite a bit of adjusting to do. 'I can only describe it as a pure culture shock,' she says with a smile. 'I had a lot to learn about Indigenous family relationships.' The kinship system determines Aboriginal social organisation and family relationships. It's a complex system that governs how people relate to each other and their roles, responsibilities and obligations in relation to one another, ceremonial business and land.

'I worked with five wonderful Indigenous health workers who helped me along the way,' Wendy says. 'I learned to understand who could marry who, who could sit next to who and who could not because of poison cousin relationships. I learned about ceremonial life, rituals around death such as sorry business and needing to close the clinic after a death to respect the deceased. I also learned about the need for ceremonial smoking of the clinic or aircraft if a patient had passed away in either of those places.'

Wendy was the only midwife and nurse. It was the wet season and the dirt airstrip was often closed due to wet weather. That meant the clinic staff sometimes had to wait for the airstrip to dry out enough for the plane to land and evacuate the sick patients.

'The heat and humidity were draining at times and the number of frogs on the verandah at my flat had to be seen to be believed – they even lived in the toilet bowl. The health-centre staff evacuated patients to Gove or Darwin and if this happened at night, we had to light kerosene flares at the airstrip for the plane to land. At first, I kept thinking, *How did I end up here?* Going bush was so outside my experience and I was quite nervous.'

It wasn't long before Wendy's triage capability was put to
the test. One night three very ill patients presented at the clinic
at once. 'A young boy aged about ten had been stung by an Iru-
kandji jellyfish – an extremely venomous box jellyfish,' Wendy
says. 'I knew the collective symptoms included excruciating
muscle cramps in the arms and legs, severe pain in the back
and kidneys, a burning sensation of the skin, headaches, nausea, sweating and vomiting. When I first saw him he was lying
limply across his mother's lap and his eyes were rolling back in
his head. I thought, *Oh no, this is not good.*'

At the same time the man who worked at the car-repair shop
needed his eyes irrigated after a pipe had burst and sprayed
hydraulic oil into his eyes. And a woman in early labour presented just after he arrived. Wendy thought, *Hell's bells! Why
does everything happen at once? It never rains, it pours.* 'I
handled the situation as best as I could. The bloke with oil in
his eyes ended up irrigating them himself under my instruc-
tion and then he helped me with the envenomated boy, whose
blood pressure had elevated. I flushed the red weals on his
abdomen with vinegar to neutralise the tentacle stinging, and
with no antivenin available, I gave him an intravenous analge-
sia for the pain.' The health workers arrived and between them
they stabilised the boy and the expectant mother before the
aeromedical retrieval crew arrived – the outcomes were good
all around.

'In hindsight, it may not have been the best decision for a
new recruit to go to a single-post remote area – but I'm so glad
I did,' she says. 'I learned that my way wasn't always the right
way and I learned to listen and absorb very quickly.'

Back at Nhulunbuy, Wendy was asked to do a two-month
stint for NTAMS. 'It was my first introduction to flight nursing,' she says. 'We'd fly out to communities to pick up patients

and bring them back to Gove. I never imagined I'd be doing that and I loved every minute. At the time it was all radio contact, which was maintained between Nhulunbuy NTAMS and the communities in East Arnhem Land in case telephone contact failed. We did twice-daily "radio scheds" with the community staff, relaying hospital inpatient reports. I'd talk to the health workers in communities about patients and organise outpatient appointments. There were three flight nurses providing a 24-hour on-call service and we were kept fairly busy. Often I'd just get home and be looking forward to climbing into bed when the pager would go off again and back out the door I'd go.'

When Wendy first started as a flight nurse she flew to a remote community with another nurse, Prue, who was training her. 'As we approached all I could see was red earth,' Wendy says. 'Like many of the airstrips out there, this one was very short. The engine noise was loud in the cabin so I was having trouble hearing Prue, who was trying to tell me what to expect. When we were about to land the pilot put the wing flaps into full flap position to prepare for the short landing strip. And down we went. We did what felt like a nosedive into this little community by a lake with an airstrip that, from the air, looked like the size of a small footpath. The steep descent frightened the heck out of me and I think I actually screamed. We landed with red dust billowing behind the plane and when we came to a halt I looked out the window to see a small tin-roofed structure. There was a bench seat in the shade and a jaunty little sign that read, *Welcome to Lake Evella Airport*.'

In those days, many flights were nurse-only and there was a fair bit of daring and dangerous flying. 'It was hot, dusty, exciting work and for me, the remote-area lifestyle was unparalleled. We'd go fishing and camping to far-flung beaches and we'd be the only people there. We knew crocodiles could be around, so we swam vigilantly and briefly in clear, shallow water. I remember swimming at a beach with a couple of nurses once and when we came out of the water the tide had receded and we saw a distinct angular jawline imprint in the sand. He was in the same water we had just emerged from.'

At the end of 1990 after her three-month stint as a flight nurse in Nhulunbuy, Wendy took a job in Darwin with NTAMS as a flight nurse and midwife, where she worked for the next three years. Darwin was a much bigger operation and nurses flew out to run clinics and for medical retrievals. With higher acuity and more critical cases, Wendy experienced some very long periods on call and a few scary evacuations.

'On one retrieval we lost a 27-week premature newborn when the baby died mid-flight,' Wendy says. 'And we had an ill baby die on a tarmac before we could get him into the plane. You don't forget those tragedies. But thankfully, there are innumerable successful evacuations that saved lives – and that's what keeps you going.'

After three years in Darwin nearing the end of 1993, Wendy found herself at a crossroads again. She applied to return to Gove as a midwife. 'I'd had enough of being on call and was missing midwifery, so I went back to maternity in Nhulunbuy. I was happy to be back at the smaller hospital, working again in midwifery and back to the lifestyle of beach trips, four-wheel driving out bush, swimming at waterholes and knowing people by face – seeing women I had helped throughout their pregnancies or during their births at the shops with their babies.' Wendy had only been back about eight months when she was asked if she could relieve in aeromedical retrievals again, and from 1995 to 2005 she did mostly flight nursing and midwifery stints at the hospital.

One morning on a first-light evacuation, Wendy and a doctor flew into an outstation south of Nhulunbuy, where a woman had given birth in the early hours of the morning and needed an aerial retrieval. 'The station had an airstrip but no light flares so we had to wait for first light to go in,' Wendy says. 'We landed on the red-dirt airstrip and the family was there to meet us in their four-wheel drive. The baby was fine and in the back on the lap of his adoring aunty. The mother was on the front seat, which was reclined. She had a retained placenta and had started to bleed. The doctor and I inserted a couple of IV drips and we had blood to give her. We were having trouble removing the placenta. Stepping in to help, the aunty stood at the side of the car holding the baby, while the doctor administered the blood and drugs for the mother. The baby's father was sitting cross-legged on the roof of the vehicle holding the blood pack. Someone took a photo of that, and to this day, it's one of my favourites. We managed to stabilise the mum and flew her out with her baby.'

Wendy's work colleague and long-time friend Catherine Hurley remembers her time working with Wendy at Nhulunbuy. 'Wendy is someone who gets things done,' she says. 'She's a quiet achiever and good-humoured – people want to be with her. She's great at getting the best out of everyone and she's an excellent midwife who's admired by her peers. If there was a crisis, Wendy was the one you'd want to be with.'

Once Catherine and Wendy went off for a day of swimming to a beach out of town. 'I managed to get the car hopelessly bogged,' says Catherine. 'No one knew where we were and no one missed us. So we had to spend a long, uncomfortable night on the beach. It was October, and despite being in the tropics it got quite cold overnight. The only clothing we had was damp bathers, sarongs and shirts. We had a little pop-up shade tent to sleep under and took the sheepskin seat covers out of the vehicle to sleep on. The foil blankets from the first-aid kit and the toilet-roll pillows were the difference between a truly miserable night and a bearable one,' Catherine says with a laugh.

The women had to sleep far enough away from the water's edge to avoid any crocodiles that could be around, but not too far up the beach because there were free-range buffalos to worry about. 'With snatches of sleep we waited the night out,' Catherine says. 'We knew people wouldn't miss us until the next morning when we didn't show up for work. We were camped under the direct route of our medical plane's flight path and in the middle of the night we saw it fly over us heading for Darwin. We knew then that the person on duty wouldn't be there first thing in the morning – further delaying the time before someone missed us.'

Fortunately, a woman in a car came across the two flight nurses at lunchtime the next day and helped them dig the vehicle out. 'She offered us freshly baked muffins and as we'd only had a banana to share the night before, it took a lot of self-control not to take one in each hand,' Catherine says. 'It could have been wretched, but Wendy made it fun – we laughed our way through it.'

After many years with NTAMS in Nhulunbuy, Wendy felt the need to move on and have a break from the on-call lifestyle. 'At that time we did many days of either eighteen or 24 hours on call, which took its toll on the work–life balance. I often felt I was just recovering from one long on-call session and it was time to go back and do it all again. The sound of the pager going off began to jangle my nerves, and as much as I loved the flying, my thoughts again turned to purely midwifery.'

In 2002 Wendy returned to Adelaide to study neonatal intensive care nursing. She thought it was time to go back home to family and this time she thought she'd stay. But still she couldn't settle in the city. 'So I went back to Nhulunbuy and at the same time started to think about my future. A few years earlier I'd bought a unit in Cairns and I thought I might just go there. I'd always loved Cairns. With no job arranged, I moved there in 2005 and that's where I'm based now. It's such a beautiful place and my parents and family visit me often.'

Soon after settling in, Wendy got a job in midwifery at the Cairns Hospital and joined the Midwifery Outreach team visiting Cape York communities to provide antenatal care and continuity of care to those women when they came down to Cairns to give birth.

Kelly Kearns works with Wendy at the Cairns Hospital. She helped establish Team Midwifery in Cairns to set up the Outreach Midwifery service, and then another team later to solely look after the needs of the Indigenous women in the Cape York Peninsula communities. They would fly into the Cape with the consultant obstetrician for at least three days to do three or four communities in a run, once every six weeks. 'I had a list of criteria written out that I thought were the attributes the women we care for would respond to,' Kelly says. 'When Wendy started work with us, I noticed she had a lovely rapport with people. Unlike me, outspoken, she's the opposite. She's soft, loving and very giving – she's just a beautiful person. It's a privilege working with Indigenous girls and it takes a special kind of person to set up a rapport and to connect. You are working with a woman at a most difficult time of her life, so it's very important to have a strong understanding of her culture and her needs. Wendy not only has an excellent clinical background to take on this role in midwifery and to work with Indigenous women, she works from the heart.'

One day a woman and her husband and their three boys came in by bus from a town just north of Cairns for the mother's antenatal appointment. She was around 37 to 38 weeks pregnant. The bus ride was about an hour long. On the way the woman felt a few contractions but they weren't regular or painful. The bus dropped the family off at a local shopping centre and as the boys were hungry they stopped at the food court for lunch. While her family was eating, the mother's contractions grew more frequent and painful. She pressed the boys to eat up; it was time to get to the hospital.

As the family waited at the taxi rank the mother's waters broke with a gush. When the mini-bus taxi pulled in the mother climbed quickly into the small seat next to the sliding door and the boys sat in the back. Her husband sat in the front with the nervous driver. Stepping on it for the five-minute trip, the driver headed to the base hospital as fast as she could. 'She alerted the hospital that a pregnant woman was on her way and in labour,' Wendy says. 'The message came through to us in the birth suite. Another midwife and I grabbed our emergency pack and raced down to the emergency department.'

About halfway to the hospital the woman felt an overwhelming urge to push and pulled off her briefs. The worried taxi driver sped on. The woman's husband turned around to see how his wife was going and was astonished to see the baby's head emerging. He clambered over the front seat to reach his wife, tore off his T-shirt and spread it out like a sling – just in time for his baby boy to fall into it. On arrival at the ambulance bay a sea of expectant faces from the emergency department and the birth suite met the family.

The baby was crying furiously, dad was all smiles, the boys were bursting with excitement and the taxi driver was holding her chest and worried she might need assistance from the emergency department.

The mother looked at Wendy and said, 'That was very uncomfortable giving birth on that tiny little seat.' And with that, she was helped onto the stretcher and wheeled up to the birth suite, where the baby's cord was clamped and cut and the placenta delivered. Apart from the mother giving birth in a taxi, there were no complications around her son's birth and the family returned home several days later. A very proud taxi driver was interviewed and photographed the next day for the local newspaper with her special passengers. 'I love that about midwifery,' Wendy says. 'You just never know what the day will bring.'

After two years in maternity an opportunity to work with the Royal Flying Doctor Service (RFDS) in Cairns came up. 'Once again missing the flying, I began work with RFDS in 2008 and in 2010 I split jobs to work two shifts per week in maternity at the hospital and two flying shifts per week with RFDS. With the best of both worlds, I'm loving the variety between the two.' In addition, Wendy is studying Bowen Therapy, a soft-tissue body therapy, to complement her midwifery practice and, essentially, help newborn babies.

CHAPTER

9

Gayle Donaldson

Gayle Donaldson stirred from a deep sleep when her phone rang at 12.55 am. By the time she reached it, she'd missed it. She crept back into bed without waking her husband, Rob – taking the cordless phone with her. Wide awake now she started to worry. *Is Mum okay? Are the kids okay? Why is the phone ringing?* It rang again at 1.05 am. Jody, the night-shift nurse at the Alpha Hospital, was on the other end. 'Angie's waters have broken. The ambulance is bringing her in. How fast can you get here?' she asked.

Gayle tried to get her head around the call. 'Why is she at home?' she asked Jody, remembering Angie had left her cattle station a week ago to wait in Emerald (the nearest regional centre) for her baby.

'Her other three kids were in Emerald all week for the School of the Air mini-school, so Angie thought she'd take them home today and have the weekend with them before going back on Monday,' Jody explained.

Gayle dressed quickly and kissed Rob goodbye. As a nurse and midwife based at the Alpha Hospital in the central Queensland highlands, she needed to hurry. It was mid-winter and overnight temperatures could plunge. It was three degrees.

Gayle ran across to the shed and tried to open the Toyota door, but it was locked. 'I thought, *What the hell? We never lock cars*,' Gayle says. It turned out Rob had locked it because they were heading off to Brisbane the next day for their eldest daughter Laura's 21st birthday and their bags were in there. Gayle hunted for the keys. They weren't where they should have been. She darted back into the house. She found them and rushed back to the Toyota. Then she noticed there was hardly any fuel in the tank. Alpha, a tiny rural town, which locals refer to as 'The Gateway to the West', sits on the Capricorn Highway 168 kilometres west of Emerald and 930 kilometres north-west of Brisbane. And it's an hour's drive from Gayle's cattle station, so being low on fuel was a problem.

Gayle had to quickly decide what to do. 'I thought, *Do I spend ten minutes putting diesel in or just go?* I decided to go. I could fuel up in town for the drive back.' While dodging kangaroos and cattle on the road along the way, Gayle went over and over labour and birthing procedures in her mind. She hadn't birthed a baby for several years – not since Alpha's facility had closed in 1995, forcing expectant mothers to leave home to wait for their babies in larger centres. 'I thought, *I have no warmers. Oh God, I hope we can keep the baby warm.*' She was also thinking how glad she was that she'd just done a midwifery update course through CRANAplus (an organisation to support health professionals working in rural and remote Australia). It was still fresh in her mind.

Gayle arrived at the hospital at 2.15 am and rushed into the ward to find Angie surrounded by nurses and her husband, Andy. She greeted them cheerfully. Everyone looked to her with relief on their faces. 'Outwardly I stayed calm,' she says. 'Inwardly, I was nervous and stressed.' But with experience and training kicking in, Gayle instantly knew what she needed to do. She began taking the obs, checking the labour stage and the baby. Everything was fine and the labour and birth went smoothly. 'At 3.18 am we welcomed a gorgeous baby boy, making it two girls and two boys for Angie and Andy.'

But it wasn't quite over. 'The placenta was not delivering,' Gayle says. They waited an hour, but nothing happened. After several telephone talks with obstetricians, they decided they needed to take the two-hour trip to Emerald by ambulance. Luckily, an ambulance from a bigger centre was already there – they had a hospital on wheels.

Gayle hopped in with Angie and her baby and Lea, the director of nursing (DON), followed in Gayle's Toyota. Halfway to Emerald when they reached the turn-off to Gayle's cattle property, Medway Station, they swapped. Lea joined Angie in the ambulance and Gayle drove into her homestead. She was exhausted and freezing cold, but still running on adrenaline. There was no time to sleep – she and Rob had a plane to catch in a few hours' time. 'I was worried about Angie, so I texted Lea to make sure everything was okay.'

The ambulance arrived in Emerald as the sun was rising. The placenta still hadn't delivered, so Angie was taken into theatre, where it was removed without complication. Later that morning on her way to the Emerald Airport, Gayle called into the hospital. She filled out the birth registration forms and had a little time to check on Angie and her baby, who were doing extremely well. 'It was a wonderful outcome and made me realise how much I miss the birthing part of midwifery.'

Angie says when she arrived at the Alpha Hospital she was feeling quite calm, despite knowing she wasn't where she should be. 'I was supposed to be in Emerald waiting for the baby there, but I really didn't mind that I ended up in Alpha,' she says. 'I'd had an uncomplicated pregnancy. I was really pleased when Gayle walked in. I've known her since my eldest child was born and it was reassuring to have her with me.'

Gayle grew up in an idyllic country lifestyle in central Queensland on a cattle property outside Rockhampton with her parents and two brothers. Moving to Brisbane in 1985 to train in nursing at the Princess Alexandra Hospital was not easy. 'I had never left home before and I was terribly home-sick,' she says. 'But I made some really lovely friends in the nurses' quarters and they looked out for me and convinced me to stay. I travelled home on the bus quite often and when I started going out with a Japanese boy in my second year, I got over the homesickness.'

Though the relationship became serious, when Gayle went to Japan to meet her boyfriend's parents, she discovered they were wealthy and had already planned an arranged marriage for their son.

'So I finished my final year carrying a broken heart. But my lovely friends looked after me and I poured myself into the study.' Gayle went on to sit the state exam and topped the class. 'I was a bit of a dork, but I still enjoyed taking part in the antics. One day the girls sent me off to theatre to collect some fallopian tubes. I fell for their tricks every time.'

Gayle's training was hospital-based, so she spent six weeks learning the ropes before being 'let loose on the general pub-lic', as she describes it. 'We were supervised, but really just got thrown in the deep end.' Gayle finished training in 1988. 'If we'd had to go to university I probably wouldn't have been able to do nursing. My parents didn't believe in tertiary education and probably couldn't have afforded to send me. They were of the mind that you just finished school and got a job – that's just how it was.'

Gayle returned to Rockhampton to work at the Base Hospital. 'I was put to work in theatre, but I didn't really like it. It's a very sterile environment and everyone's asleep. I preferred the patient contact. So I applied for a job at Aramac, a small, rural town in the Barcaldine Shire and 530 kilometres west of Rockhampton. I worked there for seventeen months and got my first taste of working in a remote hospital.' At the time, women could still have their babies in Aramac, so Gayle had the opportunity to help out with quite a few births and it was here she saw a baby born for the first time. 'I felt very emotional,' Gayle recalls. 'I looked at the woman and her partner and could see so much love between them at that moment. It hit home how incredible it was when new life came into the world, particularly when you are part of it. I knew then I wanted midwifery to play a large part in my career. I realised, too, that even though most circumstances are happy, there are often times when it can be a bit sad. Sometimes you see beautiful babies born and then when you carry them out to the car on discharge, you see the family situations are not always ideal for a newborn child.'

Before the 1990s, all the small hospitals had maternity wards for delivering babies. Gayle realised if she wanted to continue with rural nursing, midwifery was going to be an essential part of her career.

Outback Queensland was new to Gayle and she took to the lifestyle quickly. In Aramac something new happened every day. 'The variety was amazing – we dealt with whatever came through the door. There were busy periods and quiet periods and my social life was always busy. There was something on every weekend – a B&S ball to get to, someone's property to visit. I had a boyfriend who worked on a sheep property out of Aramac and I used to visit him.'

Gayle moved to Townsville to do her twelve-month midwifery course at the former Kirwin Women's Hospital . Alternating between antenatal, postnatal and labour wards and clinics, it was hands-on learning. 'I loved everything about it and this is where I did my first independent delivery.' It was on 26 September 1990. It was the mother's first baby and the labour was fairly long. Gayle had looked after the mother through her shift and stayed back after work to be with her for the birth. She was very keen to do her first birth. After all, that's why she was there. As she tended to the woman and the birth drew close, Gayle was extremely nervous and worried. 'I thought, *I just want to get this done. I want it to be over, so I can get on with things.*' Everything went to plan and Gayle helped birth a little girl weighing 2.66 kilograms. But she forgot to milk the blood from between the two clamps before the father cut the umbilical cord. When he cut it, blood sprayed everywhere, creating momentary chaos. 'I only made that mistake once. I can remember the father wasn't a lot of help really – but at least he was there. I felt relieved afterwards and then I just wanted to do more.'

For Gayle, the best thing about working in maternity is that 98 per cent of the time the outcome is good. 'Most of the time it's a well woman having a beautiful, healthy baby. In Townsville, I'd be in the shopping centre and people would come up to me to say hello and show me how their baby has grown. I'd often forget their names – but they were always very grateful – it's such a lovely area to work in.'

In Townsville Gayle met Liz Jane, who was in her midwifery group. Liz remembers Gayle as the country girl come to live in the city to train for her mid. 'Gayle was the most naive young woman I'd met. You could string her along over anything. Blessed with an infectious, sunny nature, she assumed good in everybody. Coming to Townsville was a bit of a wake-up call for her. It was an army town and some confronting cases were coming through the wards. They weren't all beautiful families having babies. We had to deal with some pretty rough stuff.'

The midwives in training were eager to notch up their twenty required births to pass. 'In the maternity ward it's one on one and you are on duty for eight hours – you're taking obs, over-seeing an epidural, holding hands tightly, talking through the labour and finally a little head is on view. One day this had all happened to me and just as I put the gloves on to birth the baby, the tyrant nurse-in-charge walked in with a young, glib-looking medical student. *Gloves off, nurse*, she said. *This student doctor will deliver.* I was furious. After all my hard yards, he would deliver and I'd be sent back in later for the post-care and clean-up. I went down to the pan room to vent some anguish and Gayle walked in.

'*What's wrong, Liz?* she asked. I told her how Dr Smooth had taken over. She understood and agreed he and the tyrant nurse were awful.

'*Would you like me to go down there and distract him, Liz? I'll get him out of the room and you can duck back in and deliver that baby.*

'Gayle was serious – she would have done that for me. What's more, as a stunning 22-year-old, she would have suc-ceeded. The next day I told the other midwives what had hap-pened and what a great friend Gayle was – so loyal and sweet. Then weeks later when we were on night duty, Dr Smooth was in the corner reading some papers. He looked up and saw Gayle. *Hey, Gayle,* he said, *I hear you want to see me?*

'Gayle glared at me, red-faced. She was mortified. The rest of us fell about laughing. Gayle was very easy to play a joke on – she was always the victim. But we did all look after one another and Gayle and I have been dear friends ever since.'

Gayle's second birth experience soon after the first was another little girl. 'When you are birthing a baby you focus so much on what's happening with the mother and the baby, you become oblivious to whatever else is happening in the room. I remember going to the postnatal ward every day after my first few births to check on the babies. They were very special to me.'

The scariest experience Gayle had in Townsville was cutting her first episiotomy. 'I had to cut the perineum to make it easier for the baby to birth. I put in a local anaesthetic and then cut where the skin is very thick. I was glad when I got the first one of those done, too.'

Gayle loved the labour ward, but her charge nurse was very fierce. 'Gosh we were made to do some terrible jobs,' she says. 'I remember a weekend chore for the student midwives was to clean the "placenta muncher". But we always seemed to laugh when we did it, even though it was disgusting. It was a tough twelve months all in all, but we stuck together and supported each other. We had to learn it all in such a short time – then pass state exams.'

With midwifery completed, Gayle got a job at the Alpha Hospital, where she still works part-time today. 'When I started it was a busy little hospital and the infamous flying obstetrician Jim Baker would fly in regularly.' The late Jim Baker set up the Roma-based program in Queensland's southern inland region in conjunction with Queensland Health in 1988. He would fly to any one of 30 hospitals spread across the vast distances of the state's country areas. 'We often had to wait for him to fly in for emergencies or if there was a complication with a birth,' Gayle says. 'He was a larger-than-life character and he made a big difference to the delivery of health care in the bush. It meant women didn't have to travel out – he'd come to them. And he was always available to give advice on the phone. Time and again we were relieved to see Dr Baker step off the plane – whether it be for an emergency caesarian, a retained placenta or perhaps a forceps delivery. I know for sure that that man saved the lives of many babies and mothers in outback Queensland.

In addition to Jim Baker, Longreach-based doctor Bob Spence would fly in every four to six weeks to perform surgical procedures, and there was also a full-time doctor, Melissa Butini, who's now a highly qualified obstetrician at the Wesley Hospital in Brisbane. Alpha could be a hectic place, and because there were only two midwives, Gayle would be called in regularly.

Very soon after Gayle started at the Alpha Hospital an obstetric emergency took place and she was brusquely introduced to maternity in the outback. It was fortunate that on the day, two midwives were on duty, including Gayle, as well as a doctor with a keen interest in obstetrics. The mum was having her first baby and labour was going along well until an examination revealed a cord prolapse had occurred. This happens when the umbilical cord slips through the dilated cervix and into the birth canal before the baby during labour. 'The cord is baby's lifeline and if it becomes compressed by the baby's head it can be life threatening to the baby,' Gayle says. 'The treatment for a cord prolapse is to hold the baby's head away from the cord by putting the mother on her hands and knees and for the midwife or doctor to physically hold the head off the cord with their fingers. And a caesarian is usually needed as soon as possible.' In a large maternity hospital a caesarian can be organised in minutes. But in the tiny town of Alpha it was quite different. 'Staff needed to be called in to organise the theatre and the theatre nurse lived an hour out of town. Dr Jim Baker was contacted and asked to fly in as soon as he could.

'This all took time. We were all busy keeping the cord from being compressed and helping the mother and her support people to keep calm during a very scary time.'

Gayle was a newly qualified midwife accustomed to working in a major facility with everything at her fingertips – she was extremely nervous. 'The wait for everyone to arrive felt like an eternity,' she says. 'But we were very fortunate to have Melissa with us – she led us through it magnificently and we did have plenty to do while we were waiting. Melissa kept the head off the cord and we midwives and nurses prepared for the theatre sister's arrival. We got the baby warmer ready and organised someone to pick up Jim from the airport. Before he arrived, someone had to go down and clear the airstrip of kangaroos and any other obstacles. Had it been at night the lights would have had to be turned on for the plane to land. Back then, if the weather was too bad for landing, patients had to be transferred by ambulance to the larger airports at Barcaldine or Emerald. Today the airstrip is fully fenced and the lights can be turned on by the RFDS pilot flying in.'

Gayle will never forget the feeling of relief when Jim entered the theatre and scrubbed to perform the C-section. 'We all knew the baby needed to be birthed quickly and we worked as fast as we could to make it happen. Each one of us was worried for the baby. Miraculously, everything came together and through some incredible teamwork, a very healthy baby girl was handed to her mother.'

There were often some over-zealous parents. 'We'd look at the length of the birth plan when women came to the labour ward and raise our eyebrows. Most mothers and their partners drew up a birth plan of what they wanted to happen. Often some mothers – especially schoolteachers – would arrive with pages and pages of a birth plan with very strict ideas. Sadly these plans often went belly up. They would come in declaring they didn't want any pain relief and then end up with an epidural because they couldn't bear the pain. Often the labour went on for a very long time. Then you'd get the twenty-year-old woman with no plan come in and she'd birth the baby naturally after a 30-minute labour.'

Gayle advises mothers now to have a bit of an idea of what they'd like to happen, but to just go with the flow. 'I say to women, *Tell your partner what you want, but be open to whatever happens.*'

Having worked at Alpha since 1991, Gayle has started caring for expectant mothers she had delivered as babies. 'A couple of years ago I was looking over the chart for a mother I was seeing for antenatal visits when I recognised the handwriting on the card – it was mine. I realised, with a small degree of shock, I had delivered this young woman many years previously in the Alpha Hospital. That's what I love about my job now. Even though mothers don't routinely deliver in Alpha, I care for them while they are pregnant and then have the joy of watching their babies grow. If I worked in a busy labour ward, generally I would just see the birth and probably not see the baby again. In rural areas we become very involved and part of the families' lives. I think I am really lucky.'

One Sunday Gayle was at the hospital caring for a woman in labour. Being a midwife in a small town she would stay with a woman from the start of her labour until the birth and stay on until she was sure both mother and baby were well. On this day, Gayle birthed a beautiful baby boy. The dad was overjoyed as their first child was a girl and he was thrilled to be welcoming a little boy. 'After everything was sorted and mum and baby were settled, the dad popped a bottle of bubbly and was very insistent that I have a glass to celebrate the birth with them,' Gayle says. 'Now you have to remember that I had been at work for more than ten to twelve hours with very few breaks and not much food to eat. Needless to say after the bubbly I left the hospital feeling quite intoxicated – luckily I was overnighting there and didn't have to drive home.'

Gayle was born on 31 January, 1967. Her husband, Robert, was born in the same hospital the day before. They met for the first time 25 years later in Townsville. 'I gave him my phone number, but he didn't call me.' She laughs. 'Then we met again at an Australia Day ball in the Alpha town hall in 1992. He was helping his brother Ian on one of the family cattle properties out of town and ended up going to the B&S ball. 'When I saw him again I thought, *He is hot. I really need to get to know him.*' They danced most of the night and the next day Rob rang the Alpha Hospital and asked to speak to Gayle. 'In those days there were no mobile phones, so he had to ring the hospital and ask to be put through to the nurses' quarters. It took a bit of courage on his part. Then he came to visit me and bought me a rose for Valentine's Day and before long we started dating, despite being a few hours' drive from each other. He was living at the property he grew up on near Capella in central Queensland most of the time, but worked on whichever family place needed him most. He was unmarried and with quite a few family properties in the area he got shifted about a lot.'

Rob and Gayle married a year after they met in Rockhampton. They flew to Melbourne for their honeymoon, hired a car and drove to Canberra. It was a new experience for both of them. Born and raised in the country, neither had travelled much outside Queensland. 'We drove through all the little rural towns off the beaten track and stayed in country pubs,' says Gayle.

The young married couple moved into Medway, a 20,500-hectare cattle station near Bogantungan, west of Emerald and just below the ridge of the Great Dividing Range. 'When we married we were part of a big Donaldson family partnership and Robert's father ran all the family properties. I continued to work five days a fortnight at Alpha.' Just over a year after they married, Rob and Gayle had their first child, Laura in 1994. Gayle was 27. 'I took maternity leave and when Laura was nine months old I fell pregnant with twin boys. That was a surprise. By this time you couldn't have your first baby in Alpha, so Laura was born in Emerald and with early twinges I was sent to Rockhampton at 32 weeks to wait for the twins. Sam and Hastings arrived naturally and without complication and weighed over seven pounds [3.1 kilograms]. This was the practical component of midwifery. I returned home with three children under two. I'm sure I'm a more compassionate midwife having had my own children. I remember things I said to expectant mothers when I was 22 and think gosh, it's a wonder they didn't deck me. I'd say, *Now come on, it's just that burning feeling, just push through it.* Yes, it's a lot more than a burning feeling.'

Gayle returned to work at a small clinic in the little town of Jericho when Laura was four years old and the twins were three. 'I took the children in with me and lived in town during the week. The kids stayed with a family day-care mum during the day and she would even stay on call for me overnight. She'd come at any hour if I was called out. She'd get the kids and I'd go off in the ambulance. It was mad really. Having a babysitter was the only way I could do it and I was determined to work. She was a wonderful girl.'

The clinic at Jericho was almost always busy. The nurse Gayle filled in for said Gayle had the ambulance constantly on the go whenever she came in. 'One Friday a doctor on duty at the clinic rang me and asked if I could come quickly. I could hear panic in his voice and as I made my way over to the clinic, I was wondering what on earth could be wrong.' Gayle rushed into the consulting room to find the doctor and his patient (a pregnant woman) sitting on the examination bed with their legs up and looking petrified. They pointed at the fridge. 'On close examination I found a huge brown snake. It was spring and I guess it must have been hibernating around the warm fridge motor over the winter. The days were warming up and it had clearly decided it was time to emerge.' It was an unusual situation and caused a lot of excitement. Gayle is used to seeing snakes and they don't frighten her, but that doesn't mean she likes to get too close. She got all the patients in the waiting room out into the street and called the local garage man who came over to capture and release the frightened snake.

On another occasion in Jericho Gayle was able to assist a young junior doctor who had just arrived. She was checking a young baby that was fully breastfed. The mum was a first-time mother and had lots of questions. She told the doctor that the baby hadn't opened its bowels for six days and before that, had gone eight days without a poo. 'Young doctors were sent to rural areas fresh out of uni and a lot was expected of them,' Gayle says. 'Our young doctor was very concerned about the baby and ready to send it on to a bigger centre for further assessment. As a midwife I was able to help out by advising that it was quite normal for a fully breastfed baby to go up to 10 days without doing a poo. The guidelines we go by for fully breastfed babies are that they can poo up to ten times a day or once every ten days. Health care in rural areas really is a team effort. Times have changed a bit now and there is a lot more support for doctors practising in rural areas.'

Laura remembers the trips to Jericho well. 'Mum would pile us all in the car and off we'd go – we didn't care, we just wanted to be with her and with each other. We grew up spending a lot of time travelling in four-wheel drives over dirt roads to clinics and hospitals,' Laura says. 'I remember on my sixth birthday we called into the Alpha Bakery on the way to Jericho to pick up my birthday cake. We hung around the clinic all day eating cake and doing our school work. We liked going there because the people next door had a really cool treehouse and let us play in it. Mum didn't have much sympathy for any of us when we got sick. Once I cut my arm open and because we lived too far from a hospital, Mum stitched me up with a Steri-Strip – you know that bandage they use to pull the skin together to close small wounds. I still have the scar.'

Families living in isolated areas form extraordinarily close relationships. And it's clear the Donaldson family has done just this. Laura said she knew that no matter what sort of day her mother had had, she would still put others first and never let her personal life affect her work. 'She's a very compassionate person and gives hours of her time – including voluntary work for bush kids away at camps. At home our phone was often ringing for Mum – and still does. I'd recognise the names of women ringing a lot during their pregnancies or when they had little kids – they'd ring Mum for every little thing to ask her advice. They'd say, *Do you think I should take him or her to hospital?* And Mum would say, *No, it's just a cold.* But if there was something serious going on, she'd be there for them.'

At Jericho, Gayle saw everything from maternity and babies to horse, farming and road accidents. 'I loved the antenatal and postnatal work. I didn't like being away from home, but the day care worked for me. Accessing day care in rural areas is often impossible, so I was lucky.'

After a few years in Jericho Gayle was asked to work in the Alpha Hospital again and she signed on for two days a fortnight. Due to the long-distance travel her days are usually consecutive. But it's unusual for her to only do two days because due to short staffing at the hospital, she is often called on to work extra shifts.

'I fell pregnant with my fourth child and Bella was born in 2002. When the kids were small I did my child health training externally through the New South Wales College of Nursing. It was mostly theory, reading and assignments and without internet access it was hard. Gaining qualifications and upskilling can be difficult when you live in the bush.' Gayle is often asked to join a video conference with work via Longreach. 'I could do it from home, but a three-hour session would be impossible with our extremely limited internet-download capacity. So I have to drive to town whenever something like that is needed.' In between droughts, fires and floods, it took Gayle two years to graduate in child and adolescent health.

Before leaving home for boarding school, Gayle's children learned through distance education from their preschool years through to Year 7. It began with Laura in 1999. Gayle juggled work with weekend and night shifts in Alpha, leaving the kids with Rob. 'I wasn't a dedicated home tutor,' Gayle says. 'Over the years we've had nannies, backpackers and governesses to help teach – I'd have to step in if we didn't have one. Home-schooling four children made life very busy and to cope, we had to be extremely organised. I kept working because I loved it – and I think it kept me sane. Every year we looked forward to a Volunteers for Isolated Students' Education (VISE) teacher, who would take over the schoolroom for six weeks. We had some amazing teachers pass through our schoolroom.'

Staff at the Alpha Hospital have always been very supportive and child friendly, which was wonderful for Gayle, who sometimes didn't have the child care she needed. 'There were times when Robert was away and I'd have to take the kids into the hospital and they'd sleep in there with me. If they were short-staffed when Bella was a baby I would take her in, put her to sleep in a cot, work and then take her home in the morning. One night she was asleep and I had to do an ambulance transfer to Emerald. When she woke up in the morning, she didn't even know I had gone.'

Gayle's son Hastings was accident prone, and one day while he was in the outpatients' waiting room he split his head open. 'No one knows what happened. There was blood everywhere and we were grateful we were in the hospital and able to glue him straight up.'

One night when Gayle's shift was almost over and she was preparing for the handover, the front doorbell rang. She assumed it was the night staff arriving. 'I kept writing and a few seconds later I heard my name being called by a lovely young mother I knew well. *Gayle, I need you. Now!* I rushed out to find her holding her flat, pale, unresponsive baby. She said, *I accidentally gave him rice. He's allergic to it and this is what happens. I didn't know the food I gave him had rice in it.* She was so distressed.

'While I was making an assessment the night staff arrived – it was Jody. The baby's airway was clear and there were no breathing problems, but the poor little fellow was vomiting profusely. He had nothing left in his tummy – he was vomiting coffee grounds [a term for old blood] and there were small flecks of new blood. This meant he had some kind of gastric irritation.

'Without a resident doctor we dialled Telehealth [a video-conferencing medical service for rural and regional areas] for assistance. A team of doctors from a neonatal ward talked to us and looked at the baby. It was a great help and very reassuring for us. They organised the baby's hospital transfer. About four hours later a doctor reviewed the baby and the allergy subsided. The mum has since seen a specialist and found the baby has an adverse food reaction involving the immune system, called food protein-induced enterocolitis syndrome [FPIES]. I had never heard of it. I had been seeing the baby since he was born and knew he was having some problems and not steadily gaining weight. It was a relief to know the cause and to be able to turn his condition around.'

Being an outback nurse means having to improvise in unusual circumstances. Being a highly trusted one also means sometimes extending your skills to treat creatures other than humans. One day one of the nurses brought her small dog that had delivered six puppies. 'A few days post-delivery the dog started having seizures. A common treatment at the time for seizures was Valium, so I gave the dog some, and lots of it. It didn't stop having seizures, so I rang Rob's brother, who is a vet in New South Wales. I told him the symptoms and he said the dog had milk fever and the treatment was calcium, not Valium. When I told him how much Valium I had given the dog, he was surprised the poor thing was still alive.' Gayle had an intravenous line into the dog, so they gave her the pre-scribed calcium and she stopped having seizures. Mother and puppies all survived.

On a more serious occasion, after a full day of seeing expect-ant mothers and babies at a midwifery child health clinic day at the Alpha Hospital, Gayle was called out. 'It was school and university holidays so Laura was in with me doing some "assistant in nursing" work and Bella had come in to play cards with the elderly patients. Laura and Bella drove home about 4 pm and I was finishing up when suddenly Jody burst into the room and asked for our DON [director of nursing], Lea. *We have an ambulance call-out to a local property. They're doing CPR on a nineteen-year-old.* We all snapped into emergency mode. Lea and her partner, Michael, grabbed gear and knowing the seriousness Lea asked if I could come along, too.' With lights flashing and the siren blaring, they reached the cattle station within 30 minutes. On route Lea and Gayle worked through an advanced life-support plan of action. 'We all knew the people who lived on the property and I prayed the whole way, knowing that was wrong, that it would be a stranger. We got there and tried to revive the patient. Our attempts were unsuccessful and the beautiful young man, who we all did know, didn't make it. It was devastating. It had been a freak motorbike accident – he hadn't been doing anything wrong. I had visited this boy and his mother in hospital when he was born. He played footy with my boys. I'd given him his school vaccines. He was a special young man and loved by everyone who knew him. The grief was heartbreaking, and his widespread community fell into mourning. The accident was hard-hitting and changed my view of life. Our boys do the same kind of station work as this boy had done. I hug my kids whenever I can and tell them I love them every day.'

With their beef cattle operation well developed now, Rob is kept extremely busy running Droughtmaster and Charolais cross cattle and Gayle helps out when she's needed. Nurses tend to get roped into a lot of volunteering for bush events, so the long, dusty road trips are still common for Gayle. Each year she volunteers as duty nurse for the week-long Isolated Children's Parents' Association (ICPA) sports camp held for geographically isolated students. Laura says every year at the ICPA camp Gayle is up most nights with sick kids. 'Then she patches them up during the day from sport injuries. It's a long week for Mum, but she enjoys catching up with all the other distance education mums.'

Gayle also attended a kids' camp in Brisbane, which came about at the request of her son Hastings, who attends boarding school in the city. Most of the children at the camp had profound disabilities and Hastings offered to care for a young boy over the week. His school's older students spent the time helping the children participate in sport and activities and the volunteer nurses were on hand. Not only is it a wonderful week for the children, the caregivers are given a week's respite. Gayle flew down and loved every minute of her week helping out. 'Times like this remind me of the fragility of life and the magic of human connection.'

10

Olivia Bigham

When Olivia Bigham arrived in Benin, West Africa, a Mercy Ships' staffer was there to meet her. She had changed into her Mercy Ships T-shirt on board the plane from Paris so that she was identifiable when she walked into the airport. Olivia had arrived to work as a volunteer nurse on the floating hospital, the *Africa Mercy*. Inside the airport she met two other young people wearing the same T-shirts, and like Olivia they were excited. The three were escorted directly from the airport and driven through the town to the ship, which was docked at the massive Cotonou Port that sits on the west coast of Africa. Great lines of shipping containers on trucks paved the way. It was late at night and unsafe for them to be out. Olivia later learned that one half of the town was opulent and the other was a poor shantytown inhabited by extremely underprivileged people.

But on arrival Olivia had little idea about the port city and walked behind the others along a massive gangway to be met by the ship's purser and Gurkha security guards. Her luggage had been left behind in Paris due to a flight delay, and despite looking forward to this new adventure, she was tired but filled with nervous excitement. 'Our passports were taken and we were issued with a photo ID card and told to keep it on us at all times. I knew safety was a priority and we needed to take measures to avoid kidnapping or injury.' Gradually overwhelmed with nervous anticipation, she wondered if she'd made the right decision. 'I thought, *This is more intense than I expected.*'

Shown to her cabin, she met her bunkmate, Claire, who had arrived earlier that day and had claimed the bottom bunk. Like a naval ship, it had a six-bunk cabin and the crew was English-speaking people from around 30 countries, with the bulk from America and England. They made up the 450 or so people who lived on the ship. 'With Claire it was instant friendship and my spirits lifted the minute we met. It took my bag a couple of days to arrive from Paris and Claire shared her toiletries and clothes with me. Following an induction, we began work a few days later.' Astounded by so many different terms, medications and unfamiliar equipment, Olivia was grateful to meet and become friends with Carlissa, an American girl who helped her decipher all things new.

It was 2009 and Olivia was 31 when she left Tasmania to work as a volunteer nurse with Mercy Ships. It was quite a culture shock compared to her small island home in the southern hemisphere. Mercy Ships bring first-class medical care to the world's poorest nations. The medical services are free for people suffering illness or injury, usually as a result of abject poverty. Because she had trauma-nursing experience, Olivia was assigned a ward nurse to work with adults, paediatrics and in the intensive care unit (ICU). 'I worked in orthopedics, surgery and we saw a lot of cleft palates in babies and young children. The surgeries performed depended on which doctors and surgeons were on board, but included eye surgery, plastic constructive surgery and facial surgery for tumours and deformities – most of which are rarely seen in the West. The lack of medical services and prohibitive cost of medical care resulted in very large tumours requiring major surgery.'

A large number of women suffer from a condition called veso-vaginal fistula (VVF), which is usually correctible by surgery. 'If a woman experiences a prolonged labour without medical assistance, the babies often die from obstruction,' she explains. 'The pressure of the head causes skin breaks between the vagina, the urethra and the rectum and forms a hole. This leads to the mother losing control of their urine, menstrual blood and faeces. And when this happens they're regarded as dirty and ostracised from their communities.'

Before the ship docks at the port, an assessment day is organised and patients are given a yellow card and a surgery date. Hundreds of women come in with vaginal fistulas and are looked after post-op, usually for up to 21 days. Then they can go home, and in most cases, they're accepted back into their communities. 'The day they leave the ship is amazing,' Olivia says. 'They are "dry" – no more "leaking" – and they celebrate like there's no tomorrow. A special ceremony is held and they're given a new dress and hat and they literally sing and dance their way off the ship. It's just beautiful to see and I loved joining in with the singing and dancing along with them if I was invited. Women who were so physically afflicted – experiencing so much joy after their operation. While I was there more than a hundred surgeries were performed.'

The *Africa Mercy* is a floating blood bank and Olivia had to donate blood on two occasions. 'I'm type B negative,' she says. 'In Australia only about two percent of the population has this blood type. But in Benin it was one of the most common. Captain Tim and I were kept on the ship if there was a big surgery planned for a patient with our blood type. Once our blood was directly transferred into a critically ill man with a huge umbilical hernia – he survived.'

With any sign of civil unrest the self-contained hospital and crew can quickly evacuate. 'Because it's a floating hospital, it can dock at any port,' Olivia says. 'Volunteer staff pay their way to work on board, which lowers the overheads – it's a charitable organisation. It flies under a Maltese flag rather than the United States – which was important to my dad when I applied,' she says. 'The threat of pirates and terror plots had him worried and that safety measure placated him a little.'

Her decision to work in Africa came as a surprise to her parents, Jeanette and Peter, but they knew she was determined to go. 'Olivia is a born leader and from a young age she had direction,' Jeanette says. 'She was always very focused and took things seriously. She wanted to do her best at everything she tried and at times we worried she was pushing herself too much. We'd try to rein her in a little. But she's strong and very determined. In primary school she sang and danced competitively and was good at drama and we thought she'd go down that path. But eventually it became clear that nursing was her calling.'

Olivia grew up attending the Baptist church in Launceston and that's where she heard about the Mercy Ships and the need for volunteer medical crew. Having already worked in the Philippines and Kenya as a nurse, she googled Mercy Ships to find out more and applied for a three-month stint.

While Olivia experienced a couple of daunting moments, working on the ship was truly rewarding. It's also where she met South African midwife Kate. 'Kate is the reason I decided to become a midwife,' Olivia says. 'She transferred her passion and enthusiasm for midwifery to me. She said she could see me as a midwife and that I needed to go and do it.' Olivia and Andi, who was the other Australian nurse on board, both studied midwifery after falling under the influence of Kate.

'I developed resilience and gained more confidence working in Benin. It was an inspiring experience and one I'll always be grateful for.' Olivia returned to Tasmania and spent the next twelve months studying for her midwifery at the Royal Hobart Hospital.

She jokes about the first time she helped birth a newborn. She was very young and staying at her grandparents' sheep-and-cattle farm at Cluan Tiers, near the small town of Westbury in northern Tasmania. She was watching a sheep birthing twin lambs. 'The first lamb came out and then one hoof emerged, but not the other. My papa said, *Put your hand in, Olivia and get that other hoof out.* I did what he asked and pulled the other twin out. That's what you do on a farm,' she says, laughing.

Olivia began her nursing training with the University of Tasmania and the Royal Hobart Hospital in 1996. She worked as a student midwife at Hobart Private Hospital and studied midwifery externally through Charles Sturt University at Wagga Wagga. It was in Hobart that she saw a baby birthed for the first time. 'I remember thinking, *Oh, so that's how it happens?* I wasn't totally fascinated with it. But I did feel honoured to be a part of that.'

After her training, Olivia took a job at Launceston General Hospital and clocked up experience across several wards. 'The only reason I got that job was because the woman who interviewed me knew my family and was my Sunday-school teacher when I was a kid. She knew I'd be a good worker.'

In her graduation year Olivia became addicted to emergency care. 'I really enjoyed that and ended up moving to Melbourne to do my trauma training,' she says. 'I had a fabulous clinical lecturer, Lisa, who helped me through. I wouldn't have done it without her. She was one of those positive people who make you think you can do anything. We're still friends.' Olivia applied for an emergency position at Dandenong Hospital and at 22 it was a massive change for her. 'I liked the diversity. They say emergency nurses know a little bit about a lot of stuff. Every hour and day was different.' Within a few years Olivia was promoted to acting nurse-in-charge, which requires a good dose of skill and responsibility. You also need to be an effective communicator, extremely organised and able to roll with the punches. She stayed in Melbourne for eight years and spent most of her time in resuscitation, trauma and triage.

It was the emergency experience that helped prepare Olivia for overseas volunteer work. In 2003, at 27, she took a three-month placement with World Youth International (WYI) in Western Kenya outside the tiny town of Ugunja and close to the Uganda border. Based around the city of Kisumu, along the edge of Lake Victoria, and providing vital medical care to underprivileged communities, her work was also a unique opportunity to gain valuable experience.

When she drove into the little village, the fact that she was the only medical worker in her group began to hit home. Technically, volunteers can't go into Kenya as a nurse. The WYI group's official task was to build a school and community hall and Olivia entered as a volunteer worker. But as a trained nurse she knew she would not be able to help treating anyone that came through the door. In a country ravaged by HIV/AIDS and malaria and where people don't have access to the most basic treatment, Olivia knew she would face new challenges. When she arrived she drew on her strengths as a capable emergency care worker and nurse-in-charge.

Mindful of local customs, she had to be aware of the local medicine men. 'We were careful not to step on their toes,' she says. 'From day one I saw myriad cases from slashings, stabbings and victims of violent attacks to helping out with babies, cuts and injuries and common illnesses. I discovered a mix of mud and cow dung makes really good plaster to set broken bones. I even washed out animal intestines, a main ingredient for a special broth to help people get well.'

Not long after her arrival, a man came to the church and asked Olivia to accompany him. His wife was heavily pregnant and bleeding. Olivia followed him back to his home, not sure what she'd be confronted with and hoping she could help. 'But by the time we reached her, it was too late,' she says. 'The pregnant mother died in front me. She had suffered from placenta previa, where the placenta covers the cervix. She needed a caesarian – you can't birth the placenta before the baby.' When Olivia walked out of the little hut she found the woman's other three children happily playing. 'It was heartbreaking,' she says. 'They didn't know their mother had died. I can still see the faces of the mother and father and each of the children. The mother's family came in and took over and it was very obvious when it was time for me to leave. This was the sad and extremely difficult side of my work there. The deaths of children in third world countries are extremely hard to handle and sad when you know most could be avoided with immediate access to health care, hospitals and doctors.'

In 2005 Olivia volunteered to work in the Philippines with the Christian organisation International Needs Australia, which is based out of Melbourne. She worked in Manila and to the south at Legazpi. And again, as the only medical person, she found it challenging professionally and personally. 'You arrive with a stethoscope and perhaps some Panadol in your bag and that's about it,' she says. 'Once I was in Kenya and the Philippines I was able to purchase medications. I'd ask a local to take my list and buy them for me because I'd be charged a fortune. But each time I work in developing countries, my skills are honed – both visual and listening and back to basic nursing skills. I always come back a better nurse from the experience.'

There are many sponsored children in Manila and Olivia spent time with them, helping to set up their schooling. 'International Needs had established quite a few community projects, like breakfast programs for schools, and our job was to help develop more. I ran a few medical clinics and just used what little resources I had. Medical care is crazy expensive. I saw acute cases of nasty infections and sores. The people understood we were limited in what we could do and were grateful for anything we could help with.'

After returning from Manila, Olivia moved back to Tasmania in 2008 and worked in the emergency department as an in-charge nurse. She completed her midwifery training in 2010 and applied for a CareFlight job in 2011. 'It was time to do something different, so I applied for the job not really expecting to get it,' she says. 'The call came a week later asking if I could start right away. I thought, *Oh no, now I have to move to Darwin!*' And she did. Soon after she packed her bags and drove from one end of Australia to the other.

It was an immense change for Olivia. 'You can't compare being in a hospital to being in an aircraft,' she says. 'The working space, the back-up or the resources just aren't there. It's just you and the pilot. When you're working independently under guidelines, the pressure is on and you need to know what you're doing. We treated anything from heart attacks to car accidents, people dying of renal failure, women birthing, sick kids and victims of domestic violence.'

For Olivia, domestic violence cases were the most confronting. 'We were called out a lot for that. Once we had to fly into a community for a man who had been assaulted by a family member. When we arrived there were more than 200 people, mostly men, waiting at the front of the clinic. We had to get in there. The doctor who had flown in with me was absolutely terrified. I said, *They're not here for us, they're here for the patient and they're looking for the man who assaulted him – we're not going to have a problem.*' And they didn't. Olivia boldly strode through the crowd. 'I saw a woman I knew and stopped to say hello, then kept walking,' she says. 'We stabilised the man and flew him to Darwin for surgery.'

When Olivia arrived in Darwin one of the first things she had to do was take an Aboriginal cultural awareness course. 'I soon realised I had to be mindful of many things. I engaged with Indigenous elders whenever I was invited to – that could have been at a clinic or when they came as a patient. It wasn't culturally okay for me to just seek them out. I didn't want to offend anybody. They'd tell me where you didn't go and what you didn't do and I had to make sure my knees were always covered. If I had a pregnant woman close to birthing on a plane, I wouldn't divert to pick anyone else up. We couldn't have a male on board at the same time. Birthing babies was strictly women's business. I wanted to learn as much as I could and that meant spending a lot of time talking with the local Indigenous people in each community and I was guided by their advice.'

Assisting women in labour could be extremely testing. 'It was common for very young girls to be pregnant,' she says. 'Trying to explain what's going on could be very difficult. It wasn't always a happy situation. Sometimes it was a matter of having someone to hold a hand. A lot of the time there was no one to do that. Many of the pregnant women who needed to fly were frightened of the plane. I'd sit right next to them and stay by their side. The young women always had a support person fly with them – an aunty, sister or grandmother. Whether you're an expectant mum having a baby in Launceston or a remote community, you need somebody with you.'

Olivia's first week in Darwin gave her a taste of what lay ahead as a flight midwife. 'I flew to one of the Tiwi Islands north of Darwin to assist a mother who had gone into labour. I realised we probably wouldn't get her back to Darwin on time, so we prepared for her to birth the baby in the clinic. Better there than in the aircraft. With minimal fuss and great joy, the young mother birthed a baby boy on the floor of the clinic. Her aunty told me it was the first baby born on country for the last five years and everyone was ecstatic.'

That day happened to be the Tiwi football grand final and the town was overflowing with people. Before Olivia left the clinic for the airport with the mother and baby to transfer them back to Darwin, the family asked Olivia if she could drive the mother past the football ground on the way. 'We drove slowly past the footy ground and from the back of the troopy I had to hold the baby up at the window for everyone to see. As we drove past people clapped and cheered and kids ran along behind us. I said to the pilot, *Oh my gosh, I can't believe this.*

He laughed and said, *Welcome to Tiwi, Olivia.*' Everybody knew the baby had been born on country and it caused huge excitement. 'It was clearly a special event and I felt really honoured to have been a part of that,' Olivia says.

Not long after Olivia was tasked to fly into an Aboriginal community south of Darwin near a croc-infested river. A woman had lost one of her fingers to a crocodile while hunting for Arafura file snakes in the mangroves. 'She also suffered a mangled right hand and leg wounds. It's thought she probably grabbed the croc by mistake as attacks by freshwater crocodiles are rare. But in the real crocodile-infested parts, people are crazy. They fish standing in water up to their knees in areas inhabited by six-metre crocs. I was called out to a few croc attacks while I was there, but sadly the victims didn't survive – they rarely do. It reminded us how very real it was.'

The daily tasks with CareFlight were diverse. 'One day I flew to Bullo River Station, which my grandparents had told me about. We flew out a stockman who had been crushed between two Brahman bulls. He was okay and lucky it wasn't worse.' When CareFlight planes fly into cattle stations, they often land on four paddocks. The fences are moved for the planes so the pilot can land in the middle, then taxi along with the wings going over the height of fences, which are made especially to accommodate the planes. The plane then shuttles snuggly between the gates all the way up to the shed. 'The pilots thought that was the coolest thing ever – and we didn't have to walk far,' Olivia says.

On the day she flew to Bullo Station, Olivia was working with one of her favourite pilots. 'On our way in we had such a great aerial view of the station and impossibly beautiful landscape.' Bullo Station spans more than half a million acres and is close to the Western Australian border, about 78 kilometres north-west of Timber Creek and 115 kilometres north-east of Kununurra. The Victoria River flows through the property from the Bullo Gorge for over 80 kilometres. 'From the air we crossed rugged ochre mountain ranges, meandering rivers and waterholes blanketed with pink and white lilies. We saw flocks of galahs, solitary eagles, kangaroos and feral pigs. I knew this was something special. Sadly, my grandparents had died before I moved to Darwin – I was sad I couldn't tell them about my flight into Bullo River Station.'

Knowing the CareFlight King Air aircraft had two engines and the pilots were extremely skilled, Olivia didn't have any fear of flying. She trusted the pilots implicitly. 'I am in awe of them,' she says. 'They pitch in and help without asking. They know where things are and unpack for you. At the Bullo job, I realised I'd left a little machine on the plane and turned to walk back to get it. But the pilot knew I'd need it and had already gone back for it. They're also very protective of the flight nurses – we don't go anywhere alone, they constantly watch out for us.'

Olivia was regularly tasked to work at Nhulunbuy on the Gove Peninsula in the Northern Territory. 'I'd be sent out there with a pilot to work at the non-doctored base for a week.' While there was a lot of seriousness to the work in Darwin, there was also a lighter side. 'One of my favourite days was Territory Day. It's like Australia Day, but the Territory's own. You can set off as many firecrackers as you want, wherever you want, from 6 pm until midnight. It's like flying over a war zone. The noise, colour and excitement are all encompassing. And of course, there are injuries every year – a finger lost, a leg burnt. Darwin is four hours from everywhere except Perth. On holidays, I'd fly to a capital city somewhere to meet friends or family who'd also fly in.

'I worked with some fantastic pilots and medical crew and appreciated the chance to do it. I love to help people and to be given the chance to do a job like that was wonderful. Every day was an amazing day and I was very proud to wear the CareFlight uniform.'

In January 2014, after three years in Darwin, Olivia took the long drive back to Tasmania in her Subaru Outback with her personalised number plate *SUBARU*. 'Everyone has personalised plates in Darwin, so I thought I might as well join the majority. I drove via Uluru and Kings Canyon – places I'd always wanted to see up close,' she says.

Back in Tasmania, Olivia returned to midwifery at the Hobart Private Hospital and also worked in emergency at the Royal Hobart Hospital. At times she uses her midwifery skills in emergency or her emergency skills in midwifery. Recently she birthed her 100th baby, who turned out to be the brother of a little girl that she had helped bring into the world. 'I had nursed his sister four years before. It was special because I knew the family well and it was nice for them to have a midwife they knew. I'm part of a scheme called Know Your Midwife (KYM), where women alternate visits between the obstetrician and the KYM midwife. The idea is that one of us will be on hand to birth the baby.'

Each of those one hundred births and more was unique and for Olivia each new birth continues to be fresh and exciting. Recently she had been eagerly waiting all night for a text to ping. It came in at 9 am. The expectant mother under her care had been admitted the day before following an induction. Olivia had met with the couple several times to talk about their birth expectations.

The expectant father had texted Olivia to let her know the labour had begun. She had been involved with the family since she was a student of midwifery and was about to help birth the couple's fourth child. She had helped birth two of their other three children and was thrilled to be here for this one. The couple's first child, a girl, was birthed by a caesarian section (or C-section) before Olivia had become a midwife; the second was a successful vaginal birth after a C-section (VBAC) when Olivia was a student and the third child was another VBAC with Olivia. With the risk of the C-section scar tearing, careful consideration had been given to the best birthing plan for this baby.

When Olivia stepped into the warm, quiet room just before the mother's contractions had started, she was glad to find there was some time to talk more about what the mother wanted for this baby's birth. 'She smiled at me and said, *I'm happy to go with the flow. My faith in you is a hundred per cent.* The dad vigorously nodded in agreement.'

Totally focused and calm, the woman's trust in her experienced midwife was clear. As Olivia watched the woman stand and lean into her husband to work through the contractions, she was moved by their instinctive teamwork and love. 'The dad tenderly held her through it and kept hugging her. They knew I was there,' Olivia says. 'But as one of my mid teachers told me once, midwives need to learn to knit, crochet and sit on their hands. I can do all three.'

After a three-and-a-half-hour labour, the doctor still hadn't arrived. The protocol is to notify the doctor when the baby is expected to birth soon, but on this occasion he wasn't able to make it on time. The midwives birth the babies and if everything is normal, the doctors are just on hand. Generally, the midwife and the woman have built a trusting relationship over time.

Everything was going so well and Olivia was excited to think she was going to be able to birth the baby on her own. And suddenly, without fuss or complication, a baby girl was birthed into her hands. She lifted the baby and softly spoke to the mum. 'Open your eyes.' The mother reached for her baby and placed her against her chest. Filled with emotion, she looked up at Olivia and whispered, 'Thank you. We're calling her Florence Olivia Faith.' Olivia was deeply moved. 'I thought, *This is incredible. Everything is as it should be.* The dad was excitedly cuddling his wife and brand-new little girl and we were all in tears. It was an experience I will never forget,' Olivia says.

Despite enjoying working in Tasmania again and particularly being able to spend time with her close family and friends, Olivia's longing for adventure doesn't let up. She also facilitates on the Remote Emergency Care training course with CRANAplus at remote locations around Australia. 'I mainly teach patient transfers (boat, land and air), maternal emergencies, airway emergencies, envenomation (for example, snakebite), spinal and basic life support.' But what's next? 'I'd like to work for my friend Christie, who I met on the Mercy Ship. She runs a maternity hospital on the Tanzanian–Kenyan border. Her stories are amazing and she never writes that it's volatile or unsafe. It probably won't be long before I head off again.'

Jo Hunter

When Jo Hunter's phone rang early one Sunday morning at her Blue Mountains home to let her know an expectant mother she had been caring for had gone into labour, she grabbed her kit, raced out the door and jumped into her car. She had spent the past seven months caring for the mother, who was pregnant with her second child, and had come to know the family very well. She was excited. The couple's daughter, Amity, just three years of age, had been involved in all the antenatal appointments at their home. She had loved helping midwife Jo gently palpate her mother's abdomen to check the baby's growth and position. And she'd loved taking a turn of the blood pressure cuff and stethoscope and using the Doppler to find her brother's heartbeat.

Amity and her father greeted Jo at the door. Wide-eyed and clearly thrilled, they led her through to the mother who, having started contractions, had moved from the shower to a mattress on the floor. Jo knew Amity's parents had spent a lot of time preparing her for what happens during labour and birth. 'It was left up to Amity to decide if she wanted to be present,' Jo says. 'She was adamant she did and said if it happened at night she wanted to be woken up. As I walked in I thought, *I wonder how she's feeling and if she still wants to stay to watch the water birth*. Her mum and dad had an alternative plan of support if she chose not to be there on the day.'

Amity sat down on the mattress next to her mum and began softly massaging her shoulders and rubbing her back. 'When the time came to hop into the birthing pool the mum relaxed into the water and continued to labour beautifully. Amity set about filling her mum's glass with water and offering regular sips.' The labour was fast and after just four hours of established labour the mother's contractions changed to pushing.

'The baby emerged slowly and beautifully in the water,' Jo says. 'Amity stood beside me the entire time with a look of wonder on her face as she watched him emerge. When his head was half out she announced excitedly, *The baby's head is coming out of Mummy's vagina!*' And with that her gorgeous little baby brother was born into his mother's hands. Together with her mum and dad, Amity was exhilarated.

Then, interested in the third stage, Amity donned gloves and inspected the placenta with Jo. Jo has a head torch she wears when checking whether or not stitches are needed. 'While I was doing this, Amity was intrigued. She asked me what I was doing. I said, *I'm just checking to see if Mummy's vagina is okay after pushing the baby out*. And this explanation satisfied her. Mum didn't need stitches, so I took off the head torch and went into the bathroom to get a pad.' When Jo walked back into the room, Amity had the head torch on and was closely inspecting her mum's vagina. 'Her mum smiled and rolled her eyes at me. *It's all fun and games in this house*, she said. I couldn't help thinking, *I wonder if Amity might one day become a midwife*.'

Jo is a midwife in private practice. Based in the Blue Mountains, she provides one-to-one midwifery care for women who plan to birth at home. She delivers care in a holistic manner across the antenatal, labour, birth and postnatal periods. 'I start giving care to women from the early stage of their pregnancies right through to six weeks post-birth.' She provides complete maternity care for about 30 to 40 women a year from a variety of social, economic and cultural backgrounds. 'The youngest mother I have cared for was fifteen years old and the oldest, 48 years old.'

Jo's passion is to support women who strive to achieve a normal, natural birth. 'This not only includes women considered low-risk or expecting their first baby, but also those who have experienced previous caesarian births, a postpartum haemorrhage (PPH) or physical and emotional trauma.' With a caseload of two to four women birthing per month, Jo works full-time with the care provided in the woman's home. In Jo's view, pregnancy and birth are a normal state for healthy women and an integral part of family life. Midwifery is trust based and built on a strong belief in partnerships with childbearing women and their families, as well as respecting birth as a natural process and a normal life event.

One day Jo attended a birth with a woman experiencing some emotional problems. 'When she first came to me I could see she was a quiet, private woman and I liked her immediately,' Jo says. 'At eight to ten centimetres dilated and nearing the end of labour, she seemed to be caught in transition.' When women cry out, *I can't do this anymore, I want to go home*, or if they are at home, *I want go to hospital*, it is a sign that the birth is imminent, that labour is getting tough and they simply want it to be over. It's at this stage when the support team moves in close and offers more encouragement. 'It was no different with this woman, however her distress was at a high level and labour didn't seem to be progressing. I knew she wouldn't be okay with an examination – she didn't want any touching at all.'

When the woman's family left the room, she opened up to Jo. 'She said, *I just want to talk. And I just want you to listen.* I held her hand and in a flood of tears she revealed to me that she was frightened. She said she was worried the baby was going to be a boy because the men in her family were evil. They had sexually abused her and she was scared if she had a boy, then somehow the evil would carry through to her child. After sharing her fear with me, her mood lifted and she continued to labour.'

After her emotional release the mother asked Jo to give her five minutes alone. 'I left the room and joined her family outside. Almost right away we heard her cry out during a contraction, and moments later we heard a baby's cry. We walked back in and there she was in the birth pool holding her baby boy. She had birthed and lifted him out of the water. And instantly, she fell madly in love with him. Often we have to work out what's holding the labour up – is it physical or emotional? I think experiences like this show the power of the mind.'

Jo was born in Tunbridge Wells in the United Kingdom in 1971. The youngest of five children, she immigrated to Australia with her family on the Ten Pound Poms scheme when she was three years old. In a bid to attract more skilled English people to Australia, the government offered trips for whole families. One full fare was charged and every other person paid ten pounds. 'We took six weeks to arrive by sea – I guess we were the original boat people,' Jo says, laughing. When she finished school Jo became a preschool teacher and a few years later travelled extensively through Europe, where she worked as a mothercraft nurse with families with new babies. She returned to Australia three years on with an English boyfriend, Phil, who she married in 1994. Jo continued preschool teaching before falling pregnant in 1996. 'My sister-in-law had had a homebirth and I desperately wanted one, too,' Jo says. 'But we had absolutely no money to pay for a midwife.'

Jo's first baby was born in a birth centre in Sydney, and while the birth was straightforward, she experienced problems in the third stage during the placenta delivery. 'I requested a physiological third stage; this means allowing the body to do the job of birthing the placenta in its own time without drugs [Syntocinon], fundal massage [manipulation of the postpartum uterus] or controlled cord traction [pulling on the cord] – all of which are required with active management of the third stage. The midwife on shift thought a physiological third stage just meant not giving Syntocinon to help expel the placenta. She continued with controlled cord traction and in doing so, pulled the cord off, leaving the placenta inside me.' This resulted in the need for Jo to be taken to theatre and given a general anaesthetic to manually remove the placenta. She also experienced a PPH and lost a massive 1500 millilitres of blood, which meant a blood transfusion was needed. 'At the time I was deemed high risk due to the PPH, even though it was caused by third-stage mismanagement. This meant I would have to have my next baby in a labour ward and not a birth centre.'

When Jo fell pregnant again she felt strong and well and determined to homebirth. She and Phil saved every penny so Jo could have a homebirth with the midwife of her choice. 'I went on to have three babies at home with the same midwife. I was supported to achieve an uninterrupted, drug-free, exhilarating and empowered childbirth,' she says exultantly. And this is when Jo's passion for supporting pregnant and birthing women was ignited. She could see the benefits of woman-centred, one-to-one care and homebirths. 'I completed a course and became a childbirth educator and a doula – a birth companion who assists a woman before, during and after childbirth, as well as providing physical assistance and emotional support for the woman's spouse and family.

'After I had my second baby we moved from Sydney's inner west to the Blue Mountains, where I had two more babies. My midwife travelled to be with me at my homebirths and my best friend and doula, Lu McCarthy, was at the births of my three youngest children.' Jai is now nineteen, Bronte seventeen, Riley fifteen, and Maya is fourteen. Lu says Jo has been her mentor and go-to person since they met when they were both pregnant with their first babies in Sydney. They now live about five minutes from each other and their eldest two children are the same age. Their families are extremely close, and their children have grown up together.

Lu says people gravitate to Jo's warm nature and sense of humour. 'She's also very grounding,' she adds. 'And that's what I love about her. Having worked in maternity wards in hospitals, the first thing I noticed about Jo was the way she connects and responds to pregnant women. It's something I hadn't seen in a hospital environment, which is more clinical and regulated. She quickly gains trust and expectant mums thrive under her assuring nature and professional care. Jo has been my mentor whether it's personal or work related. We have supported one another at each other's births.'

When Jo's son Riley was born, her midwife was late arriving because Jo's labour was very fast. Lu was thrilled about that. 'I made it to her place just in time,' she says. 'We were both heavily pregnant and when it was clear Riley was about to birth, I hitched up my pregnancy overalls and stepped into the pool just in time to catch him. Jo was totally focused and strong and it was a speedy, uncomplicated birth. I think Phil was glad I was there. It was amazing and of course there were floods of happy, emotional tears.'

When Jo started work as a doula, she attended two to three births a month in the hospital system and ran private antenatal classes that quickly grew in popularity. Her classes were consistently full and this is where a lot of her doula work originated. 'Women would come to class and ask if I'd be their support person at the birth,' she says. 'In the last three years of my work as a doula the local homebirth midwife asked me if I'd like to work with her. She employed me and together with her I attended two to three homebirths a month for about three years. I'd wanted to study midwifery for a long time, but with so many little kids – four born in just over five years – it was difficult. I wasn't in the headspace or in a financial position to return to study.'

But when Maya turned five and started school Jo enrolled to study midwifery. It was the second year of the direct-entry course at the only university in New South Wales offering a three-year Bachelor of Midwifery without a prerequisite nursing degree. 'Before that students had to do a three-year nursing degree and an eighteen-month postgraduate midwifery course. I studied with the intention of becoming a homebirth midwife and with no intention of working in a hospital.'

When Jo was having her babies she became closely involved in the homebirth movement as a consumer activist. The national convener of Home Birth Australia (HBA) for five years, she lobbied government and advocated for homebirths

and homebirth families. The system had moved from state to
national registration and all health professionals had to have
indemnity insurance in order to register. 'The problem was there
was no insurance protection for midwives in private practice.
The latest statistics show there are 270 homebirth midwives
around Australia – not enough for it to be financially viable for
an insurance company. When we could see we weren't going to
get anywhere, we organised a rally.'

Despite blustery, cold winds and pelting rain, the 'Mother of
all Rallies' drew more than 3000 homebirth supporters from
across Australia. Laden with banners, babies, prams and signs,
people turned up at Parliament House in Canberra to protest
over the government's refusal to extend medical insurance for
homebirths. It was a massive plea for non-intervention homebirthing and Jo was thrilled.

It was September 2009 and she, along with many others,
had been lobbying hard for a better system for some time. As
one of the 'Mother of all Rallies' coordinators, she couldn't
believe the turnout. She knew things were going well when
she heard airlines had gone into meltdown because they
didn't have enough baby carriers on board flights. 'People
braved drenching rain,' Jo says. 'They were chanting *homebirth rocks* and declared they'd haunt the Health Minis-
ter Nicola Roxon over the government's refusal to insure
homebirths.'

Nicola Roxon announced just before the rally that she
would put an exemption for requiring insurance for intrapar-
tum care in place for private-practice midwives for the next
two years while a solution was sought. Since then the exemption has been extended again and it's now due to expire in
2016. 'The College of Midwives is trying to find a solution.
It's a worldwide problem – not just in Australia. While there is

insurance for antenatal and postnatal care, there isn't any for the actual birthing. It's not a perfect system yet.'

In her third year of midwifery Jo decided to resign from HBA in preparation for her move into a professional role as a midwife. 'I felt I needed to draw a distinct line between the professional role and the consumer role,' she explains. 'I found that quite difficult because I generally look at things from a consumer perspective. But I realised that could cloud my view on a professional level. I still find this a challenge.'

When she finished her degree, the fact that she had worked with HBA and with a midwife for several years meant she had a sound idea of how to set up a private practice. 'I hadn't been doing clinical work like listening to babies' heartbeats or vaginal examinations, but I had attended births and supported women physically and emotionally during and after pregnancy for many years.'

With this competent, all-round understanding of midwifery, in 2009 Jo set up her own private practice in the Blue Mountains. 'I knew all of the Sydney homebirth midwives, which gave me an excellent support network of women. I could call on them at any time if I needed advice or assistance at a birth. Going straight into private practice, I was very lucky to have that advantage. To be honest I thought my first year in private practice would be quiet and take time to build. But I think because I'd attended so many births as a doula, when the women went on to have their next baby and the midwife I'd worked with had retired, I was the next person to call on. From the outset I was flat out.'

Jo delivers her midwifery services in homes and travels a wide boundary for antenatal, birth care and postnatal care. 'The whole idea of homebirth is to do everything at home – to stay in your own environment and maintain the control.

I think women are more comfortable in their own homes. I try not to take on more than three women a month, but sometimes there are more because there are so few midwives in private practice. I often need to work seven days a week, depending on how many women have birthed recently. It can get crazy busy when babies are born close to each other and I'm seeing women from twelve weeks pregnant through to six weeks postnatal. Occasionally it's quiet and I can have two or three days off a week. It ebbs and flows.'

Jo's daughter Bronte says having a parent that can disappear at any moment can affect family life at times. 'I was about three when Mum started being on call and we're used to her coming and going – that's just part of the midwife's job and everyone understands that. If she's on call we have to be somewhere close to home so she can get to the women quickly and the phone is always on the loudest ring. Once we were away camping and Mum was on call. She ended up going to two different births while we were camping so she was actually not there for most of the trip. It was quite funny. We just know she's got to do what she's got to do.'

Quite often Jo is called away from home – or perhaps from a wedding, a family dinner or some kind of special event. Her husband, Phil, is a project engineer and works Monday to Friday. He steps in to help Jo whenever he's needed. 'He's incredibly supportive of what I do and takes the family reins if I need to be gone for a long time,' Jo says. 'Sometimes I can be gone for several days. Phil just takes over. It can be difficult at times, but the positives far outweigh the negatives – midwifery is incredibly rewarding.'

To assist as back-up midwife when Jo needs a break, she calls on her dear friend and colleague Jacqui Wood. Jacquie was a homebirth midwife in New Zealand and then moved to

Australia in 2008. Recently, she took time out from her private practice to work in the justice system as a midwife, where she looks after pregnant women in prison. 'She's my back-up and loves attending the occasional homebirth that I can't get to. I do have to plan holidays nine months in advance and don't take on any women if their babies are due when I know I'll be on holidays. That wouldn't be fair. Women hand-pick their midwives and are paying a reasonable amount of money to have the person of their choice at the birth. So I take two weeks either side of the holiday off as well in case women are overdue or birth early. It just means I have to have a big slab of time off.'

Because the women Jo works with are low-risk, which is important for homebirths, very few emergencies unfold. 'Midwives don't often work at home with high-risk pregnancies like the birth of twins, triplets or breech births. The safety assurance for me is how well you get to know a woman over the pregnancy term. With at least ten antenatal visits, each an hour long, there's a lot of time to get to know each other and for me to gain an understanding of any birthing history. An emergency is very rare in homebirths. Usually there is early warning if things are not going well, allowing plenty of time to transfer to a hospital if needed. Things can happen and we have all experienced sad outcomes and difficult births, but usually there's time to take the appropriate action.'

Getting to know each woman is vital in Jo's work. 'Women let me know what they want out of the birth, how they want it facilitated, who they want at the birth and the clinical history. I record what's going on for each woman, including any physical or emotional issues. But with only three women a month, it's easy to remember what's going on for each of them.'

Louise McKervey has had three births with Jo and is now pregnant with her fourth child. Despite now living in the remote

NSW town of Cobar, seven hours from the Blue Mountains, Louise still wants Jo as her midwife. She plans to rent a house with her family near Jo for a few weeks before her due date.

'The first baby I had was born in a hospital and Jo was training as a midwife at that time,' Louise says. 'A friend recommended I join up with Jo as part of the hospital's midwife program and that's how I got to meet her. I ended up asking Jo more questions than the doctor because I grew to trust her more. When I went into labour I had to get to the hospital and wait for staff to contact Jo to tell her I was in labour. I thought, *I can't do this without Jo.* I was so relieved when she arrived a couple of hours later and in time for the birth.'

When Jo arrived at the hospital Louise was in the bath, in labour and close to birthing her baby. 'Then suddenly the hospital midwife said, *Okay, it's time to get out of the bath.* I'm like, *What?* And she said, *There are no water births allowed here.* I tried to protest. *I'm not moving, the baby's coming.* Jo leaned over and whispered to me, *Sit on the plug, sit on the plug!*' Louise recalls, laughing.

'But the midwife pulled the plug out on me and I birthed my baby without any water in the bath. The cord was around the baby's neck so they cut the cord immediately and whipped her away for oxygen. I had to get out of the bath and into bed before they brought her back to me. I wasn't happy with that either. Jo asked me if I wanted a cup of tea and, parched, I said, *Yes I really do.* But the midwife said I couldn't have anything until the placenta came.'

Louise had requested a physiological third stage. 'The midwife asked me to give the baby to my husband and to go and have a wee. When I told her I didn't need to, she said if I didn't wee, I would have to have a catheter put in, in case my bladder was full and in the way for my placenta to get out. She said, *If you are so scared of a tiny needle after having a baby and you don't want a catheter, then you have to go and wee.* I didn't need to, so she put the catheter in and for me that was worse than the birth itself. She started massaging my tummy and pulling on the cord. There was blood everywhere and my body was in shock with a retained placenta. It was 45 minutes after the birth and on top of this I had separation anxiety from my baby. Things were happening that I hadn't wanted.'

When Louise fell pregnant for the second time, Jo was a qualified midwife in private practice. 'There was no way I was going back to a hospital,' Louise says. 'And this time, with Jo, it was completely different. Everything went perfectly. With a homebirth midwife you can have coffee on your lounge for your antenatal visits; the kids get involved – they take the blood pressure and put the Doppler on and Jo brings dolls and things for them to learn about and play with, DVDs and books – everything is so much better.'

Louise had a trouble-free water birth at home with her second baby with Jo assisting. 'My mum, who had been terrified at the thought of a homebirth for a long time, was actually hooked on it after that,' Louise says with a chuckle. 'My third baby was, however, a harder labour. The cord was around the baby's neck three times (we didn't know this of course, until he was emerging) and Jo had to quickly get him out and get him going with some oxygen. In the meantime my husband called the ambulance, but by the time it arrived the baby was feeding and pink. Jo had him settled perfectly. So that was a stressful birth, but at the same time I know he was born in the right place. My waters hadn't broken until the baby actually came. With every contraction I felt there was a jerk at the end of it. Jo said it was probably because the cord was pulling him back each time – which proved to be right. But because the waters hadn't broken he was still nice and soft and floating around. In hindsight, I think had I been in hospital I might have asked them to break my waters because I was so uncomfortable and wanted to hurry things up and that could have ended with a distressed baby. So while his birth had some complications – everything turned out well.'

Because she lives in Cobar and is unable to birth a child in the small remote town, Louise had to decide where to have her fourth child. 'Despite being able to go anywhere in Australia to choose the birthplace, we have decided to rent a house near Jo so I can have another homebirth with her. She is the midwife I know and trust. I can just ring her if I need anything or we can Skype. I'll see her early in the New Year when we go back to the Blue Mountains for a family visit and I'll have my eighteen-week ultrasound results sent through to her by the GP in Cobar. I feel a great sense of relief and calm just knowing she'll be with me again.'

It's Jo's ability to build trusting partnerships with women, as in Louise's case, that has allowed her to be so successful in her work. In addition to this, she believes that the relationship of midwife and the woman in her care doesn't have a hierarchy. 'Women should be placed at the centre of their own experience and supported to empower themselves with knowledge and skills. It's the midwife's role to have patience and trust in the innate ability of women and babies and to be comfortable and confident to support this process.'

Because in a homebirth women hand-select the people they want present during the birth and invite them into their home, this in effect empowers women and allows them control of their birth experiences. That's why Jo feels childbirth should be a feminist issue. 'Homebirth is a lot different to coming into a hospital ward where rules have to be followed. The woman can do whatever she likes when she's in her own home. Unlike doctors on scheduled hours, the midwife never leaves and she doesn't have women in other rooms she needs to go off to. Once she is there with the expectant mother, she's there for the long haul.'

The basis of midwifery philosophy is woman-centred care. And while there are set guidelines to follow, the rights of the woman come first. Jo supports the notion that midwives are autonomous care providers who work directly with a woman to assist her to make informed decisions about her care. They believe in the woman's right to informed consent and her right of refusal. 'We help her to understand the risks and benefits so she can make the best choice for herself and the baby.'

Women requesting a homebirth generally approach it from a very educated position. They do their research before contacting Jo and know what they want. 'Occasionally the men aren't on board, but I tell you what, those that start out a little resistant are the ones that become the biggest advocates by the time their baby arrives,' Jo says.

Some women may have experienced trauma in their last pregnancy and don't want to go back for seconds. It can be very rewarding when they choose a midwife, build the trust and everything goes well. 'Often you can see where things have gone awry in previous births and it's often due to intervention,' Jo says. 'A woman might be ten days overdue and an induction is recommended. But clearly the baby is not ready and ends up in distress because of the intervention. Often it results in a caesarian. While we thank God for hospitals and caesarians in emergencies, they can be overdone,' she adds. 'We've gone from a fifteen per cent caesarian rate in the 1980s to 33 per cent – that's one in three women. Pain relief messes with physiological birth. When in labour endorphins kick in to offset the pain – you can see it. The woman begins to fall asleep between contractions, which is Mother Nature giving her endorphins to help her manage the pain. But when the pain reaches, let's say, five out of ten, and a woman is given an epidural, the pain continues to rise but she's not feeling it and her endorphin levels stay stagnant. If the epidural is decreased to allow her to push to have the baby, she endures incredible pain because the endorphins haven't been rising with the pain – the hormones aren't keeping up because of intervention.'

Water births are the least stressful. 'When the baby arrives it needs to be completely submerged in water, so it's moving from water to water at the time of birth,' Jo says. 'Under water the baby is still being oxygenated with nutrient-rich blood through the umbilical cord. As soon as the baby is born and is lifted out of the water, it opens its lungs and breathes on its own.

'We don't advocate keeping the baby under water. It should be lifted out as soon as it's born. The nice thing about a water birth is that no one has to catch the baby. If the woman is in a reclining position she can simply pick the baby up on her own. Or if she's leaning over the side of the pool, I'll gently push the baby between her legs, ask her to sit back and pick up the baby herself. Almost every time, no one needs to be handling the baby apart from the mum.

'It makes sense that because the mother is submerged in water the birth is going to be less painful. The tissues are softened and stretch better, preventing or decreasing tearing. And the baby and mother can be taken out of the water quickly if there is any concern.'

Jo sees midwives as the keepers of normal birth and woman-centred care. 'We are skilled specialists in normal birth and at the same time, trained to recognise possible problems or complications. We're aware of our limitations and scope of practice and offer referral and consultation with other healthcare providers when necessary. I wholeheartedly believe in, support and advocate for one-to-one midwifery care and believe women feel safe when their midwife is self-assured and has the competence to support their choices in whatever setting they choose to birth.'

The Blue Mountains has the second-highest homebirth rate per capita in New South Wales. The highest is in Byron Bay. 'Everyone knows everyone here in the mountains; it's a lovely community,' Jo says. 'The homebirth group meets fortnightly and runs a meal roster for new mums. They take turns cooking meals and try to guarantee dinners for two weeks. They don't go into the new parents' homes – an esky is left on the front porch and members of the homebirth group just leave food, cakes, cookies in the esky, usually with a little congratulations note. They're even mindful of dietary requirements.'

On top of her private practice Jo has gone back to the books. She's studying part-time to complete her Bachelor of Midwifery honours degree through research, on private-practice midwives, at Western Sydney University. 'There's a rich body of evidence supporting the safety of a planned midwife-attended homebirth for low-risk women,' she says. In Australia private-practice midwives attend the majority of homebirths. The most recent Australian data shows 307 midwives practise privately across Australia and 270 attend births at home as the primary midwife.

'It's well known that increased intervention rates during pregnancy, labour and birth can have long-term impacts on the health for both mother and baby. By offering services to keep healthy pregnant women out of hospital, we reduce the unnecessary intervention rates and therefore improve long-term health. Maternity accounts for the biggest number of hospital bed stays. Supporting and promoting homebirth saves the government lots of money and keeps hospital beds for those who really need them.'

CHAPTER

12

Pia Croft

As Pia Croft drove through the darkness on her way from her home at Ocean Grove in Victoria to Barwon Heads, she thought about the woman who had been in her midwifery care for the past six months, and was now about to give birth. She was glad they lived so close – at two in the morning it was only a ten-minute drive away. 'I wasn't expecting the baby to come that soon,' Pia says. 'The mother had had two previous hospital births and both those babies were late at 42 weeks. I thought, *She's 39 weeks today. She'll be surprised and excited that she's about to have her first home water birth.* And I was excited to be going in as their first midwife.'

The mother's contractions began an hour before she called Pia. But no sooner had she walked through the door than the baby's head began showing. Pia observed the mother lift up her baby through the water with her husband kneeling beside them.

The baby went straight onto his mother's chest and within a few seconds she could see him breathing and moving in his new surroundings. Pia had her bag with emergency equipment and oxygen, but as with as with most times, she didn't need to open it. 'It's almost always a case of just watching the incredible moment when parents meet their babies for the first time – I'm so lucky to be a midwife and to share that magic. The woman and her husband were both relaxed and going along beautifully. They had had time to fill the pool and then five minutes after hopping in and without pain relief or fuss the baby boy was born.'

His two big brothers woke around 6.30 am and joined their parents and new baby brother in bed. 'As far as birthing experiences go, they don't come much better,' Pia says. She stayed for about four hours after the birth to make sure mother and baby were well, then left with a promise to return that evening. The mother and baby stayed at home and as their midwife, Pia made regular postnatal visits for six weeks post-birth. 'It's wonderful how they don't have to leave their home – they can relax and focus on the baby,' Pia says.

Pia was born in 1975 in Nuremberg, Germany – the eldest child of quite a lot of siblings. She grew up in a home constantly busy with birth, babies and breastfeeding. 'That's where my passion for midwifery started,' she says with a laugh. 'I'm the only child from my mother's first marriage. Mum went on to have three more babies and Dad had six more with my stepmother. I was constantly surrounded by babies – and was even present at a few of the births. I guess I was a little mum myself. I was always minding babies and helping – I loved it.'

When Pia met her husband, Chris, he was based in Hohenfels, close to Nuremberg, with the US Army. Chris had left Australia at sixteen for the United Sates where, at eighteen, he joined the army. A good-looking young man from Melbourne, he fell for the girl with long dark-blonde hair, blue eyes and vibrant nature. Pia was a shy but strong-minded young girl. And he won her heart at first glance. The two met in a pub. 'The drinking age back then was only sixteen,' Pia says, blushing. 'That's how old I was. Chris went on to Berlin and Mannheim for a while and then a year later we met again when he came back to Nuremberg. He was five years older than me and we badly wanted to stay together.' Chris decided to leave the army in 1992 during the Gulf War. However, that meant he was in Germany illegally without a work permit or a permanent visa. The only way he could stay in the country legally was to marry Pia. To help them get by until they could marry (when Pia turned eighteen), Pia decided to leave school and work at a bakery full-time to earn enough money for their own apartment. At the same time she enrolled at night school five nights a week to study for her high school diploma.

They married in 1994 and their first daughter, Freya, was born a year later. Chris and Pia went on to have another four children with the last born in 2010.

Pia had yearned to become a midwife for as long as she could remember. She applied for the midwifery school in Erlangen, close to Nuremberg, through the hospital-based system, but as her children were still quite young she was advised to wait. She found work in areas connected to midwifery so that when the time came to study it would be easier for her. 'The birthing system in Germany is quite different to Australia's,' Pia says. 'It's common in Germany for women with low-risk pregnancies to have a midwife and homebirth. High-risk women go to hospital, but a lot more babies are born at home and the national health system supports homebirths.'

In 2000 Chris felt homesick and the family made the life-changing decision to move to Melbourne. Their daughter,

Freya, went to school and her son, Thorben, began kindergarten. They didn't speak much English because Chris spoke German at home. 'It amazed us how quickly they picked it up,' Pia says. 'After a few months we couldn't even hear their accent. It was a great experience to start from scratch and we were all so happy with just the little things. Then we moved to live in Ringwood. Chris started work as a removalist and I worked at a supermarket stacking shelves and cleaning chicken ovens during the nights. I still didn't have the midwifery training I yearned for.'

A year later, in 2001, the family moved to Ocean Grove. 'We're very close to the beach and I love the community here,' Pia says. In 2002 Pia and Chris had their fourth child, Erik. 'The birthing experience was a big change for me,' Pia says. 'I didn't know how the healthcare system worked and when I went to the doctor he said I had to go to the hospital for antenatal check-ups. I turned up to the hospital but found it very intimidating. Unlike Germany where independent midwives are more the norm, I couldn't find one near me and nor could we have afforded one. It was just too difficult so I had to have Erik in a hospital – my first hospital birth.' Everything went well and Pia was back at home two hours later. She checked herself out.

After the hospital experience Pia wanted to do midwifery more than ever. In 2003 she gained a Certificate in Aged Care at the local TAFE, followed by Division 2 Nursing in 2004. This gave her the ability to work in aged care while undergoing further studies. She worked in a local aged care facility for the next four years and loved working with the elderly, which showed because she became a favourite among the residents. 'I started at Deakin University in Geelong in 2005 and came out with my nursing degree in 2007. When the kids were still little, my studies spanned five years full time with one year working in aged care, one year in TAFE nursing and three years gaining my Bachelor of Nursing.' Pia then went straight on to do her midwifery training. 'It was a really good experience and all the study over the years helped with my English.'

One of the births Pia experienced while she was training stands out in her memory. She was assisting a woman who was having her second baby. 'Her partner was with her and as a second support person she brought along her dad,' Pia says. 'This was unusual. Usually women bring along their mothers or sisters. I didn't quite know what to do with it,' Pia recalls with a laugh. 'But the labour went smoothly – and her father was incredible. He made her laugh the whole time – they clearly had a very special relationship. Usually the support person is there to calm the mother down, but he was the opposite. He was loud and he distracted her. I had never seen anything like it – and haven't since. The woman almost laughed her baby out.'

When Pia finished her training she wanted to take her family to Germany for a long visit. 'I wanted the kids to spend time with their relatives and I also wanted to reconnect with the midwives who had looked after me in Nuremberg and I was keen to compare the two maternity systems.'

They stayed in Nuremberg for six months and Pia was able to do some midwifery in-home work while they were there. 'Part of me wanted to stay in Germany, but the kids and Chris missed Australia and I guess I did, too. We were a bit torn at that stage about what to do.' When the family returned to Australia Pia got a position at the Geelong Hospital – finally and jubilantly she was able to work as a midwife.

The 10th of October 2010 is a special day for Pia and Chris. It's the day their fifth child, Lars, was born. 'I call Lars my bonus child,' Pia jokes. 'There's a big age gap between him and his older siblings, but he was our surprise bundle of joy and brought us all closer together. He was born at home in the birth pool in our bedroom in the early hours of the morning. He was my first water birth and we had my lovely midwifery colleagues and friends Lynne and Hayley with us. I finally found out how homebirths work in Australia.' Pia didn't know at the time that the date, the 10th of the 10th, would later become even more significant in her life.

In 2013 she joined a midwifery group practice in a hospital. 'A lot of hospitals have this now,' she says. 'A midwife has a case flow with generally four women in a month under her care for antenatal and postnatal visits and remains on call for birthing. I began attending homebirths and then in 2014 decided to leave and move into a private midwifery practice.'

Today she works independently through The Birth House in Geelong, which opened in 2013. 'There are four midwives using The Birth House space,' Pia says. 'For every birth, a primary midwife and a second midwife attend. Babies can be born at home or at The Birth House – it's the woman's choice. A woman can choose what she wants to do and how to do it,' Pia says. 'There is no pressure. As long as they are healthy women, birthing is something very natural and doesn't require medical intervention for the majority of births.'

Antenatal and postnatal visits are a big part of Pia's job. 'The dynamics are very different to hospital births,' she says. 'Homebirths are well prepared and the partners provide vital support. It's important to make sure there's a strong support system in place to go through labour and birth. If a hospital transfer is needed we go with them and continue our support – but this rarely happens.'

Recently a nineteen-year-old woman from Tonga was in Pia's care. Her English was limited so her sister-in-law came along to all her appointments to translate. 'I wasn't sure during the antenatal period how the birth would unfold because of the language barrier,' Pia says. 'With Australian women you can usually judge how the labour is going by the noises they make and by their breathing. But this young woman was very quiet and I found her difficult to assess. But everything went well and she had a beautiful water birth. In my experience the mothers take the baby straightaway to hold them. But instead, this woman's twin sister took the baby. Her sister-in-law told me the custom was not to give the baby straight to the mother. She needed time to rest. I learned a lot that day and was reminded about the importance of being aware and respecting cultural differences. I would have given the baby straight to her.'

Pia is often asked what would happen if two women went into labour on the same day. 'It rarely happens, but if it does there's always a midwifery colleague on hand to assist. It had never happened to me until the 10th of the 10th 2014,' she says.

September and October are busy months in midwifery – the spring babies are born nine months after Christmas, and midwives keep this in mind. 'I had booked a full-time load for September and October and because I knew it would be a busy time, I asked Chris to take the 10th of October off work in case I got called in. I wanted to make sure one of us would be at home for Lars's birthday.'

On 9 October a call came in from Liza, one of the women under Pia's care. 'Thirteen days overdue, she was desperate to birth her baby,' Pia says. 'She was booked to come in to the Geelong Birth House for the birth of her third child. She lived about an hour away. Her previous two babies were born in a hospital and this was her first experience with a private midwife.' With excitement, Liza told Pia her waters had broken – it was about 4 pm. 'In most cases labour starts within 24 hours after the waters have broken and more often within the first six hours. Liza dropped her two boys with relatives and came into The Birth House with her husband, Jason. More than six hours since her waters had broken, the contractions were still mild.'

Meanwhile on the same day, another of Pia's women, Penne, began irregular contractions. This was Penne's second pregnancy. She'd had her first son, Mandala, two years earlier at a homebirth with midwives in Melbourne. She told Pia she had been born at home and initially not wanting to copy her mother, made an appointment at a hospital when she fell pregnant the first time. But not comfortable with the clinical, anonymous feel of the hospital environment, she didn't go back.

Penne's contractions settled by the evening and she rested comfortably at home overnight. She was 37 weeks pregnant – the same stage her first baby was born. Penne and Liza were five weeks apart with their due dates. 'I didn't think for a minute they would start their labours on the same day,' Pia says.

On the morning of the 10th Pia went to The Birth House to check on Liza and Jason. At 7.23 am Liza's contractions were mild and regular, but not yet established. 'It was difficult for Liza because at two weeks overdue and disappointed the labour hadn't progressed quickly after her waters had broken, she was feeling fretful. But she and the baby were both doing well. I left knowing the labour would progress when she and her baby were ready.' Pia drove back to Ocean Grove to cuddle her own birthday boy who had turned four. 'We opened the presents together and finished decorating his special birthday cake.'

At 11 am Penne called Pia to let her know her labour was progressing. She packed her bag and left for Penne's house. 'I was looking forward to this birth,' Pia says. 'Penne's striking, cosy house featured high, exposed rafters and soft light flooded the living space – you'd think it had been built for birthing.' When Pia arrived, Penne's mother, her partner Makot and her little boy Mandala were with her, and a birth photographer was on hand to discreetly capture the occasion. The atmosphere was calm, warm and quiet. Penne's labour progress was gentle. She moved around, hopping in and out of the pool and changing positions to stay comfortable.

Around 3 pm her contractions grew stronger and closer and she stayed in the birth pool to focus on her labour work. She fell into her own zone. 'Her mother and partner took turns to give Penne drinks and support,' says Pia. 'And I got some knitting done. As French obstetrician and childbirth specialist Michel Odent said, "Midwives that keep themselves occupied during labour allow women to feel less observed to access the primitive part of their brain and birth their babies naturally with less interventions. Midwives that knit are simply doing their job, and doing well."'

Having Pia sitting nearby knitting was very calming for Penne. 'Pia and I had spent a lot of time together because I had contacted her when I was about nine weeks pregnant. My pregnancy was fairly non-eventful, so we had plenty of time to natter about all kinds of things and our friendship grew along the way. When she was with me at the birth she gave me a steady confidence that I could do it on my own and I trusted her completely. She didn't intervene or fuss over me except to check the baby's heart rate and remind me every now and then to drink water. That's just how I wanted it. She also didn't tell me that she had another mum in labour at the same time! She gave me her full attention.'

Eventually, from the intensity of Penne's contractions and her breathing sounds, Pia knew the labour was progressing well. 'At 4 pm I contacted my midwife colleague Judy to let her know we might need her to come over soon for the final stage of labour. Judy had been to see Liza at The Birth House, but her labour still hadn't established. Judy then arrived just as Penne started gently pushing her baby out into the birth pool. Her partner sat on the side of the pool holding her hand. At 5.20 pm we could see the baby's head starting to birth and by 5.24 Penne's daughter, Sabali, came into the world. Penne exultantly lifted her up and out of the water. Like most births midwives attend, there was very little for me to do apart from watch the miracle of a mother independently birthing her baby.'

Penne and Sabali stayed in the pool connecting for a little while. 'Penne birthed her placenta 30 minutes later and she just needed a little rub of her uterus to wane a small bleed,' Pia says. 'Everyone helped tuck Penne and Sabali into their prepared nest by the pool, where the whole family could snuggle up.'

Around 7.30 pm Pia received a call from Liza. Her contractions were finally progressing and growing stronger. 'At this stage I was still at Penne's house – ten minutes from The Birth House. Penne was doing exceptionally well breastfeeding her daughter. Her mother, who was one of the best support persons I had ever seen during labour, was also a nurse and she was happy to keep an eye on Penne. Usually we stay up to four hours after a birth, it depends on the circumstances of each birth. This day I felt I needed to leave a little earlier for Liza, and as I knew Penne was in good hands, I headed off to see how my other expectant mum was going.'

Pia jumped into her car and dashed off to The Birth House. It was just past 8 pm. Liza's contractions were stronger but still irregular with long breaks. 'The baby's heart rate was perfect and Liza was doing really well with some short rest periods,' Pia says. 'She was keen to get into the birth pool – the labour had been going on for 24 hours. Often the advice is not to go into the birth pool before labour is established because the water immersion can slow the labour. I think it doesn't really matter – if the labour slows down the woman can leave the pool and after some little relief return to it. In some cases water immersion can increase contractions and accelerate labour.'

After 40 minutes in the pool, to Liza's relief, her contractions increased in duration and strength. Her labour progressed fast and she became a little overwhelmed and wanted to get out of the pool again. 'The baby's heart rate was perfect, but when Liza came out of the pool the contractions slowed again. Jason and I tried to convince Liza that it was a good thing for labour to progress. We gently suggested she might be holding onto it for some reason and she just had to make the conscious decision to let go. She had undergone some personal family matters and physical issues at her last birth. This time it was completely different and we just had to remind her and keep encouraging her to let go. Then at 9.50 pm Liza felt the baby's head descending and lots of pressure. Then with Jason in the pool with her, at 10.10 pm on the 10th day of the 10th month, Liza's little girl, Athelia was born. Mother and baby were both well and Liza was overjoyed to have finally had the water birth she'd always wanted.'

It was a busy 24 hours with two of Pia's women giving birth on the same day. 'I was so happy I was able to attend both births because as the midwife, I had built close relationships with both women and their families. The next day when I told Penne and Liza about each other, it turned out they had met before.' A few weeks later Penne and Liza caught up again through The Birth House to celebrate the birth of their daughters together.

Her son Lars's fourth birthday wasn't the first family celebration Pia had missed. Over the years in the course of midwifery work, she's missed New Year's Eve and Christmas celebrations, birthdays and dinners because of call-outs. 'But Chris knows how much I love to be a midwife and how long I dreamed to become one,' Pia says with a smile. 'He doesn't complain when I pack my bag and rush out the door. He is a wonderful support. The lifestyle can be taxing on relationships and it requires a lot of patience and understanding. For me it's all worth it – even the long days and nights. I take every day as it comes and just enjoy being a homebirth midwife in Australia.'

Recently, Taryn Morgan made the decision to leave Queensland and move to Victoria. She was pregnant with her first child when her aunt recommended The Birth House in Geelong. 'There weren't a lot of options for homebirthing in Townsville and I loved the sound of The Birth House,' Taryn says. 'When I was thirteen weeks pregnant I called in for a Meet the Midwives get-together. I met Pia and we clicked right away. There was a lovely warmth about her and over the months I came to trust her completely and value her assistance. We chatted about all the birthing options and she visited me at home every few weeks for my antenatal checks. As I progressed it was found I had a complication that could have put my baby at risk of infection, so it was decided a hospital birth would be the best option. At the hospital some of the nurses were keen to take over, but Pia stayed with me. She held my hand, encouraged me and was with me when my baby was born. Then she visited me twice a day and continued my postnatal care. I had some trouble breastfeeding and Pia guided me through that, too.'

Pia says Taryn was a strong and courageous young woman. 'As she was a single mum I felt she needed some extra support during her pregnancy and post-birth. It was important for her to have continuity of care.'

During the time Pia starts care for an expectant mother –
from about three months, through to six weeks post-birth –
she builds strong relationships with the woman and her family.
'I learn about different lifestyles, work arrangements, love,
fears, dreams, vulnerabilities, respect and relationships. The
women I look after allow me into their lives and that requires
enormous trust.

'It's a unique, intimate experience to be at the birth of a baby
with a family you know. It's not just a job – it's a very special
lifestyle.'

Genevieve Brideson

Tasked with a pilot to retrieve a woman in labour with twins at 34 weeks, Royal Flying Doctor Service (RFDS) flight nurse Genevieve Brideson left her base and flew to a regional centre. Genevieve had been told the woman's observations were stable and her membranes had ruptured. The babies' foetal heart rates were fine and the woman was contracting regularly every fifteen to twenty minutes. Both of the babies were thought to be head down, one with its back upright on the right side and the other with its back to the mother's back on the left side.

The expectant mother's Bishop's score (components of dilation, effacement, consistency, position and foetal station) was seven, so it was predicted she wouldn't birth for a number of hours. 'When we arrived the ambulance was waiting at the airstrip for us,' Genevieve says. 'Usually a midwife would come as well, but the hospital was busy and didn't have a midwife to spare. At first glance I thought the mother seemed a lot further on in her labour than I had been told, so rather than unload her from the ambulance, I grabbed some equipment and climbed in to check her observations and progress.'

On closer examination and to Genevieve's shock, she felt a little foot. The first of the twins was a footling breech. 'Having never birthed a breech baby before, my first thought was, *I need more people, back-up and equipment.* I asked the ambulance crew to take the woman and I straight back to the hospital under lights and sirens.'

The pilot alerted the RFDS communications and logistics team to inform the hospital that Genevieve and the woman were on their way back. The ambulance officer had also called the hospital, but somewhere along the way the communication broke down. 'On arrival, the staff got a surprise to see us,' Genevieve says. 'The only doctor in town with obstetric experience was out of town consulting and needed to drive in. Everyone was frantic, but things were organised rapidly. Luckily, two of the hospital's senior midwives with experience in birthing breech babies were on duty. They were called into the room to assist and I handed the woman's care over to them.' Genevieve was asked to check the neonatal resuscitation trolleys and to be available to help a second GP when he arrived due to the staff shortage. 'I contacted the pilot to let him know what was happening. He was happy to wait for me because he couldn't leave without a flight nurse.

'Six hours later we returned to base with healthy twins in one humidicrib. The babies needed a small amount of oxygen to assist their breathing and were kept under observation during the flight.' A fatigued but very relieved mother was on the rear stretcher under the close eye of her midwife, Genevieve.

The second eldest of four children, Genevieve was named after a Catholic nun. She worked hard at school and from an early age wanted to do something with her life that would make a difference. 'I was fourteen when my father died and knew I needed to do something to support myself through my entire life,' she says. 'Mum didn't have a career and we kids had to take all sorts of jobs to help stay afloat. When a good friend said she was going to do nursing and wanted to be a midwife – I instinctively knew, *yes, that's what I'll do as well.*'

In the early 1980s, when nursing registration was required before midwifery training, Genevieve, who was only seventeen, and her friend started nursing together with fierce determination to succeed. 'We trained at the Royal Adelaide Hospital for three years and then completed a graduate year to finish,' Genevieve says. 'If they liked your work during training, they employed you for a graduate year. I worked in the ophthalmology, high-dependency and vascular units and stayed on to work in high-dependency after my graduate year.'

Just before her graduate year Genevieve married Andrew, a diesel mechanic she had met in Adelaide. When Andrew was offered a position in Broken Hill to start a branch for the company he worked for, Genevieve said she wouldn't move unless she could get a job. But she was a nurse, and nurses and teachers could apply for work in Broken Hill and were indeed sought after. Other vocations were kept for locals, which was the government's way of keeping young people in town.

Not having lived in the country before, let alone the outback, it was a culture shock on multiple levels for Genevieve. Located in far western New South Wales, Broken Hill's landscape is known for its post-apocalyptic appearance. Locals say depending on the season, the vast, largely flat landscape flecked with mulga trees is either dying or thriving. But the hauntingly beautiful desert-fringed, semi-arid country with intense blue skies lures painters, photographers and filmmakers from around the world.

Genevieve worked in the hospital's intensive care unit and theatre suite for the first eight months she was there. And though the townspeople were warm and welcoming, it did take some time for her and Andrew to build friendships. 'We did make some lovely friends, but it wasn't easy,' she says. 'It was very quiet and the locals were guarded about making friends with new people in town. They knew most people coming in were transient workers and would move on. I adapted quite well and learned a great deal about myself.'

To socialise, Genevieve and Andrew would often go to the Silverton Hotel on weekends, about 30 kilometres out of town. This is the site where *Mad Max* was made, and it looked exactly like it did in the film. 'It's a pretty barren place but really interesting. Broken Hill was an interesting place to live and a great place to build and gather new skills and strengths – both in work and character.'

A little of everything came through the hospital door and Genevieve observed a number of caesarian sections. 'I also made a connection with the RFDS at Broken Hill as at the hospital we flew people in and out,' she says. Night shift began at midnight and finished at 8 am. 'That was foreign to me and a little hard to get used to,' she admits. 'I applied to do a twelve-month theatre course through the Royal Adelaide while we were in Broken Hill and had to go back to Adelaide to complete it. Andrew stayed working at Broken Hill – so with a three-and-a-half-hour drive to Adelaide, there was a lot of commuting going on.' Once the course was completed Genevieve returned to Broken Hill and landed the position in charge of the theatre suite.

In 1990 Andrew changed jobs and the couple moved again – this time to Alice Springs. He was appointed branch manager of an earth-moving company. When she arrived at the Alice Springs Hospital, having worked in charge of the theatre suite in Broken Hill, Genevieve went straight to work in theatre. She was also asked to coordinate flights for patients on commercial planes to Adelaide and Darwin. The ICU could only hold intubated, ventilated patients for 24 hours and didn't have the resources or staff to look after them for longer periods. 'If the RFDS was too busy or couldn't arrange to transfer patients, the transfers were organised with the commercial airlines, in particular, Ansett Australia,' Genevieve says. 'That marked the beginning of my interest in a flight career. I often flew with the patients and sometimes returned with those that had gone down for treatment. The patients we took down were usually intubated and ventilated and accompanied by an anaesthetist and nurse – more often than not, me. I also worked in the ICU, which was a fantastic place to work as far as teamwork goes. We were making a difference and you could see your work was needed and appreciated.'

While in Alice Springs Genevieve decided to become a midwife. 'Even though I had to drop from a senior registered nurse's salary to a training midwife's salary, at least we were paid,' she says, laughing. 'We were given all the good oil, including domiciliary midwifery training. We looked after women and could stay on after the shift finished if a birth was imminent.'

Sadly, Genevieve saw a lot of intrauterine growth restriction (IUGR) babies. 'This is when the baby is smaller than it should be because it's not growing at a normal rate inside the womb. Delayed growth puts the baby at risk of certain health problems during pregnancy, birth and after birth.'

One memorable day Genevieve looked after a young, reasonably fit woman at 39 weeks who had a terrible obstetric history. Six previous pregnancies had given her four live children, one miscarriage and one neonatal death. She had experienced a postpartum haemorrhage (PPH), two premature labours and one premature rupture of membranes. 'With this pregnancy she had already been through premature labour at 28 weeks and again at 32 weeks, but both had been stopped,' Genevieve says. And with this pregnancy she had also experienced leaking fore waters (the amniotic fluid cushioning the baby's head from the pressure of labour) for five weeks, so both the woman and her baby were at risk of infection.

'The two of us had time to build a good rapport as this was the mum's sixth baby and the labour progressed smoothly,' says Genevieve. 'Usually, the speed of labour increases with more children, but when you are "grand multipara" [a woman who has had six or more pregnancies that resulted in viable births], labour slows down again.'

Genevieve was acutely aware the woman was at very high risk of another PPH. 'But after six hours, she birthed a beautiful, ten-pound two-ounce [4.6-kilogram] healthy baby girl. The placenta and membranes delivered soon after and we actively managed this stage to prevent the possible PPH. As the midwife you're there to monitor and support, but essentially the mother does all the work – which is what happened this day.'

To both the mother's surprise and Genevieve's, given the baby's weight, the mother's perineum was sore but intact. 'There were no tears, no episiotomy needed and no PPH. We were both delighted with the outcome when the odds were not really stacked in her favour.' Genevieve was even more delighted when the mum revealed the little girl would be named after her.

Genevieve loved working with the Indigenous mothers and their babies. 'The women were usually supported by their grandmothers or aunties, rather than their mothers,' she says.

'They gave clear and wise direction to the mothers and to us and their support and knowledge was really beneficial. It really helped improve my practice. If the grandmothers and or aunties thought you were at one with them, they would give you tips on how to improve and a mark for how you managed their granddaughter's labour. They taught and supported women to feed while lying in bed to try to help manage the fatigue. They also stressed the importance of staying upright during labour, rather than being pinned to a bed, because gravity helps the progress.'

Genevieve says Alice Springs was a wonderful place to learn midwifery. It was a very supportive environment and best outcomes for women and babies were always a priority. 'Interestingly, we found the most trying mothers to be the Americans and teachers,' she says, smiling. 'There were many Americans living in Alice Springs due to the military base there. The labouring mothers would come in with a long, fully prepared birth plan and husbands fully equipped with the video camera ready to take very close-up shots. They'd read up on everything and knew exactly what they wanted and how the birth should go,' she says. 'Of course, the births often didn't go to plan.'

Halfway through Genevieve's midwifery course, Andrew was offered a position with an underground mining equipment firm in Kalgoorlie, Western Australia. Located 579 kilometres east of Perth, it's Australia's largest inland city and centre of the Goldfields. Andrew went ahead while Genevieve finished her midwifery. 'I didn't particularly want to go,' she says. 'Career-wise it was sad to leave Alice Springs at that time as I loved working in the midwifery area and possibly would have moved more into the special-care nursery. High-dependency/ intensive care work has always tended to be my focus, along with looking after critical-care midwifery patients. Moreover there were only a small number of us with midwifery qualifications, so there was a bit of an expectation you'd stay and be part of the staff. But it helped that I was going to Kalgoorlie,' she says. 'At the time people in the remote areas looked out for each other's community.'

Genevieve and Andrew packed up their furniture for removal and drove to Adelaide before continuing on the long road trip to Kalgoorlie with their dog. They moved into a company house at Boulder – close to the massive Super Pit goldmine. 'Every day, when they let off a blast, the whole house would shake and everything got coated in dust,' Genevieve recalls. 'It was quite an experience. The old house wasn't quite what I was used to after our really nice home in Alice Springs – with a swimming pool. It was just as hot in Kalgoorlie, so we did miss the pool.' At the time, Kalgoorlie and Boulder were two separate towns – they've merged into one now. The town's grand historic colonial architecture is testimony to its booming gold-rush days and importance to Australia's goldmining industry.

When Genevieve and Andrew arrived in the early nineties, living expenses were high and ordinary houses came with big rents. 'We were lucky to have a company house and eventually we were upgraded to a better one.' In a twist of fate that would become one of the highlights of Genevieve's career at that point in time, the RFDS Goldfields base in Kalgoorlie was urgently looking for casual flight nurses. Genevieve knew some of the senior flight crew and because they were aware that she was a registered midwife and experienced in critical care they contacted her. 'I was planning to have a couple of months' break,' she says. 'But I started flying on a casual basis two weeks after arriving in town from Alice Springs and I absolutely loved it.' Eight months later Genevieve, at 27, moved into a full-time position with the RFDS only to discover she was pregnant with her first child. 'I had Jonathan in 1994 and Courtney was born in 1996.'

There were strict rules for pregnant flight nurses and Genevieve couldn't stay on full-time when she fell pregnant with Jonathan, but she was able work on a casual basis with the RFDS Eastern Goldfields section. 'I managed to get the rules bent a little and flew until I was eight months pregnant. Our doctors signed me off as "well" every week and as I was working with medical staff everyone knew I was in good hands. Amusingly the senior flight nurse suggested I hide from the chief medical person when I was at the Jandakot base, south of Perth. She said, *Don't be seen when you're down there – he doesn't believe in flight nurses working after 22 weeks.* So I'd stay in the hangar and not venture into the offices until it was time to fly out again.'

Late one afternoon Genevieve and a pilot were at the base waiting for an elderly patient who was to be returned to his hometown when they received notification of a woman in her fourth pregnancy who had gone into premature labour at 33 weeks. 'She had been at the local hospital we were about to fly to for three hours. Her contractions had increased and her membranes remained intact. She was on the CTG [cardiotocography] machine and the baby's heart rate was regular with good variability. The baby was cephalic presentation – head down, back anterior, and the mum had been given the first dose of Celestone [to mature the baby's lungs] and another drug to slow or stop the contractions. Her observations were satisfactory, so the decision was made to go ahead with the return of our elderly patient to his home and then to bring the labouring woman back with us for more advanced care. As usual, there wasn't a doctor on the flight.'

The midwife from the local hospital accompanied the woman to the airstrip to meet the RFDS crew. 'Our elderly gentleman was off-loaded from the aircraft and the woman loaded as quickly as possible. Her labour had increased in intensity, even though a further drug dose had been administered.'

To complicate matters and as the pilot had predicted, the weather deteriorated significantly. After handover of both patients, the pilot and Genevieve quickly closed the aircraft doors to block out the pelting rain. 'Dealing with rainwater in the aircraft is difficult without a mop; and wet linen and clothing on both the patient and the nurse is less than ideal,' Genevieve says.

On flight departure, it is policy for the ambulance officers to wait for the aircraft to leave in case the flight nurse decides the patient needs to return to the hospital or needs help with anything. 'I conducted a quick assessment of our labouring woman. With everything okay, the pilot started the engine and we took off. Once in the air, I checked on the woman again. Due to the bad weather and turbulence, I had to stay seated with the seatbelt fastened, which limited my ability to conduct a full assessment. But it was clear the woman's labour was progressing. Mid-flight she said she felt she needed to push. I thought, *Oh no this is not a good situation. I really don't want to be alone up here with a woman in active labour who could have a postpartum haemorrhage (PPH) and then a premature baby that might need resuscitation.*'

Genevieve also knew that blood and amniotic fluid could corrode the aircraft airframes and interfere with the avionics under the aircraft floor. 'So I encouraged her to breathe deeply and to blow out to help avoid pushing. Although I hadn't done a vaginal examination, this was her fourth baby, so I estimated she was probably about eight centimetres, not yet fully dilated – another reason not to push. As we neared the airport she said again that she really wanted to push. I encouraged her to keep blowing and I explained to her that if the baby birthed I'd have two patients to care for. I said, *It would be difficult to decide which of you to care for first if we have a worst-case scenario. There's no one else on board to help and we certainly don't want the pilot over here to assist!'* With sheer inner strength and mind over matter, the courageous woman made the determined decision to keep blowing to avoid pushing.

'Power of the mind prevailed (and maybe the medication finally started to work) and the baby wasn't birthed for another twenty-four hours.'

Genevieve regularly flew into rural and remote areas to retrieve women for their sit-down, those who had started labouring prematurely, or those with high blood pressure and/or premature ruptured membranes. 'We attended the full gamut of emergencies, from mining accidents, snakebites, road accidents, cattle-station accidents, farm accidents and fractured bones to women in early labour where there is no midwife available. I've stabilised people in hotel rooms, front bars and station lounge rooms. I've sat in the back of a ute with a stretcher and bags and bumped along to the station manager's house to treat someone on the floor. I've been taken to a clinic in a remote community in the back of a paddy wagon to stabilise a patient – now that was interesting! I had never been in a paddy wagon before this. Hurtling along dry, dusty, rutted roads at a rapid rate is quite an experience. In those areas the SES and ambulance crews are all volunteers, and along with the police, they keep it all going. Sometimes we had to land on the road, and they would get in and organise the safety of that. If the pilot couldn't put down at a designated airstrip the police would go along and take out the side posts so the plane could land on the road without hitting the posts with the wings. The road would be blocked off and we could see the endless trucks lining the road as we approached for landing. Even though the pilot tries to park off the road, if there's a major accident across it, everyone's held up anyway. Every experience topped up my knowledge so I'd know what to do better next time and how to improve my care of people.'

Often nurses working in remote communities are the only nurse on call 24 hours a day, seven days a week, and working on their own for six-week blocks. These nurses usually contacted the RFDS doctors for support and advice over the phone when needed. When called in to assist, the RFDS crew would deliver milk, bread, papers, pillows and blankets, medications and other resources to the nurses – anything they thought might be appreciated. 'Often the communities had to wait a fortnight or more for a pharmacy order to be flown in, so we'd take in medications to replace whatever were used on the ground. We all pulled together as part of a big team and we had a great system in place.'

It concerned Genevieve whenever she had to put a pregnant woman on an aircraft because it is never ideal for a baby to birth in the back of a plane. 'We always carefully assess women before airlifting them to find out exactly where they are at. If a birth seemed imminent, we'd stay and birth the baby there.'

With her children still young and casual flight-nurse work scarce, Genevieve began work in domiciliary midwifery in Kalgoorlie. 'When women were discharged from hospital early with their babies, the midwives would visit them in their homes for postnatal care. With the support of a wonderful obstetrician /gynaecologist who was open to new ideas and different ways of working, we began a midwifery group practice. He brought pregnancy hand-held records to Kalgoorlie, which meant women could go anywhere, interstate or to other care providers, with their own pregnancy record. As part of the midwifery team, I made house calls for postnatal and baby checks. When I had Jonathan and Courtney, the community health nurse came to visit me and it was fantastic. It worked both ways – we would sometimes go to her. In mining communities there are not a lot of older women around to help young mums. For most young couples, their parents are interstate – like ours were. So it was nice to have a nurse come to your home to care for and support you. In remote communities, everyone looks after each other.'

After more than six years in Kalgoorlie, Genevieve's family moved back to Adelaide. 'This time it was Andrew that didn't want to leave, but Jonathan was nearly five, and I was keen for the children to get to know their grandparents and relatives and go to school in Adelaide. After lots of discussion we made the move. I found work with Ashford Agency which was part of the Adelaide Community Healthcare Alliance Group. They placed me mainly in the midwifery unit. I did a fair bit of postnatal work and some in labour and birthing. Since delivering my own children and having gone through some of my own trials and tribulations, I focused more on helping mothers with breastfeeding and managing their new babies. It was a very satisfying time in my career, and to my delight a lot of the girls I'd trained with back in the eighties were there with me.'

Work at the agency was wonderful, with flexible hours when Genevieve had a young family. 'If one of my own children got sick, I could call in and the management would say, *Okay, no worries, we'll find someone else to fill that shift.* End of story. Their support was so much appreciated and very, very refreshing.'

When the agency closed in 2002, Genevieve returned to work with the RFDS at Central Operations as a flight nurse and midwife. Andrew got a job with TAFE and was based at home, so Genevieve was able to go back to flying. 'If I had a long shift or got stuck somewhere because of the weather, Andrew would be with the kids or sometimes they'd be with Family Day Care. When he was old enough, I used to get telephone calls at 10,000 feet from Jonathan saying, *Mum, where are you? When are you coming home?* He liked to know where I was and what I was doing. He was always, and still is, good at tracking me down.'

At times Genevieve relieved at the Port Augusta and Alice Springs bases and Andrew and the children would come along and experience the different areas of work. However, Genevieve stopped flying when her daughter started to cry every time her mum went out in bad weather. 'Courtney knew we were in a single-engine aircraft,' Genevieve says. 'She was afraid I wouldn't come home safely. Also, Central Operations wasn't the same as it had been when we were in Kalgoorlie. In Kalgoorlie the kids called the pilots "uncle" and were really involved in everything that was happening. We were like one big family. In Adelaide it's bigger and understandably more formal.'

Genevieve left at the end of 2007, and based on her experience in organising air transport for country patients, got a position at the Royal Adelaide as a rural liaison clinical practice consultant.

In 2009 Genevieve began an honours degree in nursing to research how flight nurses maintain their midwifery skills in order to deliver best care to pregnant and labouring women. 'It was a focus of mine at the time – to increase support for flight nurses to maintain and build their skill base. Women deserve the best possible care and those providing it need to be confident and competent.'

Genevieve's studies revealed barriers for flight nurses when it came to maintaining their skill base. 'But to the credit of a number of RFDS operating sections, they took up my suggestions,' she says. 'They now ensure flight nurses are supported in maintaining their midwifery skills and have recently run a program with flight nurses in conjunction with the University of South Australia.'

When Genevieve completed her honours degree she moved into the university sector. 'For the last five years, I've lectured across the undergraduate nursing curriculum – first to third years. I don't think I've ever worked so hard as I have at the university; the expectations are huge,' she says. 'There's research to undergo, papers to be written, grant applying, group meetings and admin duties – on top of teaching.'

Genevieve is now on leave without pay and halfway through her PhD. 'I'm exploring the way flight nurses work in Australia and New Zealand. Currently, flight nurses are largely invisible. When I first started my honours degree, to my amazement I discovered that most academics in many disciplines had no idea that 85 to 95 per cent of the time it is a flight nurse in the back of the aircraft working alone. Like most people, they assumed a doctor was on board. They didn't know a doctor only joined the flight nurse around five to ten per cent of the time. Also there is very little written about flight nursing.'

Genevieve wants to make sure the general public is aware that most of the time patients retrieved by an aeromedical service are being cared for by a flight nurse. 'If they need a doctor, one will be there,' she says. 'But nine times out of ten it's a flight nurse that has assessed the patient and made the decision about whether and which other health professionals need to be brought in. My aim is also to increase the presence of flight nurses in the peer-reviewed literature and to increase recognition and support for the work they do among their health professional colleagues. I'm not flying anymore. Those that are flying are flat out working long shifts and saving lives. I'm doing it for them. After my PhD is completed, I'd like to focus my work in a number of areas that will help people in rural and remote areas to make sure they're not forgotten when it comes to access to quality medical services. And of course, I'll always keep a focus on the aeromedical system because that's the glue that holds it all together.'

THE MIDWIVES – BRIEF PROFILES

Wendy Agars, Cairns, Queensland

At twenty-three years of age Wendy Agars boarded a Qantas jumbo jet and flew to the United Kingdom to train in midwifery at the Edinburgh Royal Infirmary, where she lived in the Florence Nightingale nurses' home. Leaving her home and family in Adelaide, Wendy was filled with misgivings about what might lie ahead. But her bold decision sparked her sense of adventure, desire to travel and extraordinary career in midwifery. From the old-fashioned training ground in Scotland she accepted a job at Royal Darwin Hospital and moved to the Northern Territory. And before the end of the year Wendy answered a call for midwives to work in East Arnhem Land. With sought-after midwifery skills and a patient, easy-going nature, Wendy has worked in myriad outback areas as a flight nurse and midwife with the Northern Territory Aerial Medical Service. She currently works with both the Royal Flying

Doctor Service (Cairns) and the Cairns Hospital in maternity. In places of extremes, the work is hot, dusty and exciting. And for Wendy, the experience of working as a midwife in remote communities is unmatched.

Catherine (Kate) Austin, Queensland

Kate Austin's extraordinary career as a midwife has seen her work in rural and remote areas from country Victoria to the Northern Territory. Tasked to focus on midwifery in remote Indigenous communities for three- to six-week stints, Kate has worked in small community clinics at Groote Eylandt in the Gulf of Carpentaria, Croker Island, Douglas Daly District, Maningrida, and Milingimbi Island in the Northern Territory and Lajamanu at Hooker Creek Station in the western Tanami Desert. Aware of just how short of midwives remote communities are, Kate is passionate about her work. Almost always the sole midwife on duty, she is on call 24/7 for childbearing women and new mothers. Kate is involved with a program called Strong Women, Strong Baby, Strong Culture where she works alongside community 'strong women'. Kate strives to provide the best outcomes, health and wellbeing for local women and their babies.

Olivia Bigham, Hobart, Tasmania

Olivia Bigham has worked as a nurse and midwife worldwide. Based in Hobart, Olivia has volunteered on the floating hospital the *Africa Mercy* in Cotonou, Benin on the west coast of Africa, in Ugunja in Western Kenya, and in the Philippines. Olivia has worked at hospitals in Tasmania and Victoria and as a flight nurse and midwife for CareFlight in Darwin. Now back in Tasmania at the Hobart Private Hospital, Olivia has helped birth more than 100 babies. Despite enjoying midwifery work in Tasmania again and spending time with her close family and friends, her thirst for adventure hasn't let up. A friend runs a maternity hospital on the Tanzanian–Kenyan border, so it might not be long before Olivia heads off again.

Genevieve Brideson, Adelaide, South Australia

Not having lived in the country before, let alone the outback, it was a culture shock for Genevieve Brideson when she and her husband Andrew left Adelaide, South Australia to work in Broken Hill in far western New South Wales. But the hauntingly beautiful desert-fringed country with intense blue skies grew on Genevieve and helped prepare her for a move to Alice Springs, where she became a midwife. Genevieve's next move was to Kalgoorlie in Western Australia where she joined the RFDS as a flight nurse and midwife and where she also had her two children with the support of a midwife and in-home care. Returning to Adelaide so the children could spend more time with extended family, Genevieve worked in the midwifery unit of the Ashford Agency. In 2002, when the agency closed, she returned to work with the RFDS. Determined to increase recognition and support for the work flight nurses and midwives do, Genevieve is now completing a PhD exploring the way flight nurses work with the aim to improve health care for people in rural and remote areas.

Chloe Coker, Adelaide, South Australia

Chloe Coker, now 31, grew up on a farm near Port Macquarie, New South Wales. Energetic, gregarious and a natural front-runner, Chloe was surprised to find she enjoyed the harshness and isolation of remote communities. Initially Chloe went to Wadeye in the Northern Territory for a two-month stint to provide relief coverage for the Christmas period and into the New

Year of 2009. This first remote community work placement turned out to be Chloe's calling. Embracing the challenge, she went on to work for the next six years in many remote areas throughout Australia. Connecting easily with the Indigenous women under her care and their families, Chloe spends as much time as she can with them, including visits to homelands. With a strong interest in Aboriginal culture, Chloe learns the language and customs and builds trust with the people in the communities she works in. Recently, Chloe began work with the RFDS in Adelaide, where she continues to provide care to women from rural and isolated areas as a midwife and nurse.

Pia Croft, Geelong, Victoria

Pia Croft's passion for midwifery stems from her childhood in Nuremberg, Germany. She grew up in a home constantly busy with birth, babies and breastfeeding, enthusiastically minding babies and toddlers, and she loved it. At fifteen years of age Pia met Australian-born Chris, a soldier with the US Army based in Nuremberg. The two married in 1994, moved to Australia in 2000 and now have five children. Having yearned to become a midwife for as long as she could remember, Pia juggled training, work and small children to graduate in 2008 with a nursing and midwifery degree. Today she works independently through The Birth House in Geelong, Victoria. Pia assists women to bring babies into the world without medical intervention where possible and has a busy schedule of antenatal and postnatal care.

Gayle Donaldson, Central Queensland

Gayle Donaldson lives on a 20,500 hectare family-owned cattle station, Medway, west of Emerald in central Queensland – just below the ridge of the Great Dividing Range. Gayle works at the tiny Alpha Hospital, an hour's drive from Medway Station.

Since marrying her husband Rob, she has travelled to work along a lonely bush road, often with one or all of her four children in tow. Living in an isolated area, Gayle and Rob's children – two girls and twin boys – learned through distance education before leaving home for boarding school to complete secondary and tertiary studies. For the love of work and midwifery, and often during floods, fires or drought, Gayle continues to ingeniously juggle children, farm duties, long-distance travel, distance education and babies.

Mark Holmes, Sydney, New South Wales

Born and raised in the small rural town of Clermont in central Queensland, Mark Holmes, now 33, was the 110th male midwife to register in Queensland. His extensive career in midwifery has seen him train in Edinburgh, Scotland, before working at Cairns Hospital in Far North Queensland, and then returning to Clermont for a twelve-month stint in his close-knit community. In 2009 he landed a job with NSW Ambulance as a flight nurse and midwife based in Sydney, flying into rural and remote areas. It was the job he'd been hankering for since he'd experienced his own aeromedical transfer to a tertiary hospital when he was ten years old and living in the bush. Upbeat, highly skilled and compassionate, Mark is aware of the gender difference in a female-dominated job. To counteract this he goes out of his way to build trusting relationships with the women in his care.

Jo Hunter, Blue Mountains, New South Wales

Jo Hunter has worked with new families since 1990. Jo worked first as a mothercraft nurse in the UK, then as a birth and postnatal doula and childbirth educator. Today Jo is a midwife in private practice supporting families who choose to birth at home. She lives with her husband and four children in the Blue Mountains, which has the second-highest homebirth rate per capita in NSW (after Byron Bay). Her first daughter was born in water at a birth centre in Sydney and her following three were born at home. Jo's passion is to support women who strive to achieve a natural birth. With a caseload of two to four women birthing per month Jo works full-time to provide care in the woman's home. With her warm and assuring nature, Jo has a gift when it comes to connecting with and responding to pregnant women. She wholeheartedly advocates for one-to-one midwifery care and says women feel safe when their midwife is self-assured and has the competence to support their choices in whatever setting they choose to birth.

Lane Johnson, Darwin, Northern Territory

Lane had longed to become a flight nurse ever since she saw a RFDS stand at the Sydney Royal Easter Show. That was it. That was her dream. At 25 years of age she landed a job as a nurse and midwife with CareFlight Darwin. Funny, expressive and extremely competent in her work, she is known among her colleagues as a disaster magnet. Lane has faced and coped with several medical emergencies while on her own in the back of a small plane. But working alongside exceptional bush pilots, she makes a vital difference to the lives of women and families living in remote communities in the Northern Territory. Despite the challenges of extreme weather, distance and limited medical resources, she loves every minute of her midwifery job.

Marg McDonald-Ashe, South Australia

Marg McDonald-Ashe is a mobile family health nurse and midwife with Remote and Isolated Children's Exercise (RICE). Going by four-wheel drive, often travelling alone, she brings child health care and antenatal and postnatal care to women living on outback cattle stations in South Australia. Her visits might include checks for a C-section wound, mastitis or breast-feeding problems or help for someone suffering from postnatal depression. In desert country, coloured by stony, red earth and wildflowers, she traverses places like Mannahill, Broken Hill, Birdsville, Oodnadatta, Strzelecki Track, Marree, the Flinders Ranges and along the edge of the Lake Eyre basin. Through-out her career Marg has worked as a midwife in rural and remote areas, including Aboriginal communities in Central Australia and country hospitals in the United Kingdom and Canada. Recently acknowledged for her health work in the outback, Marg exemplifies the pioneering work people still do in the bush. With limited resources, she does the hard yards in extreme country – and she is deeply appreciated by women in the outback, who are aware of her determination to help and her exceptional midwifery skills.

Joy Motter, Fitzroy Crossing, Western Australia

At 72, Joy Motter is a retired midwife living in Badgingarra, WA. In 1968, at 24 years of age, Joy made her way from coun-try Victoria to the Fitzroy Crossing Hospital in the Kimberley region of Western Australia, unfazed by the unknown, for the start of an extraordinary life adventure. When Joy married a local stockman, Jim, she moved to a one-million-acre cattle station where she became nurse and midwife for more than 60 workers and their families living on the property. Without elec-tricity, TV, air conditioning or even a telephone, the only com-munication was by radio through the RFDS. Travel in the wet season was by plane only and in the build-up it was hot, sticky and fraught with insect explosions. Despite the challenges of isolation Joy warmed to the Crossing the minute she arrived.

With a practical, determined and tireless nature, she rolled up her sleeves and got on with the job. Through years of working in extremely harsh conditions, Joy dealt with both difficult and joyous midwifery cases for the mostly Indigenous women under her care. Cherished by everyone who knew her, she knew how to balance the fine line of being an active local and keeping a professional distance when she was needed instead as a trusted and confidential health professional.

Lisa Peberdy, Queensland

Lisa Peberdy grew up on Queensland's Sunshine Coast. She has worked as a midwife in rural and remote areas across Western Australia, the Northern Territory and Queensland, and in 1999 she volunteered to assist in East Timor in the wake of the humanitarian and security crisis. Working out of Thursday Island Hospital, Lisa flew regularly to the outer islands in the Torres Strait archipelago to provide health care. From Mount Isa, Lisa ran outreach clinics across the Queensland Gulf region in conjunction with the RFDS. With a strong understanding of the challenges women in remote areas face, Lisa has driven long distances in a jam-packed LandCruiser, mostly on her own, to far-flung locations, working in very basic conditions – but with her quirky sense of humour and sunny disposition, that has never discouraged her. Lisa's stand-out skills as a midwife and her determined nature make a difference to the lives of many women living in isolated areas.

ACKNOWLEDGEMENTS

Firstly, my heartfelt thanks to the midwives in this book for sharing their incredible stories. Each of them mentioned to me the importance they placed on building trust with the women in their care. I am so grateful to them for trusting me with their stories and the time they gave me during their busy schedules and call-outs.

A special thanks to Lane Johnson for her generosity of time and kindness to me during my stay in Nhulunbuy and Darwin. And thanks to two of the world's nicest and best pilots, Ben Ragg and Matthew Mommers (CareFlight), for their vital contribution. Thanks also to Nhulunbuy-based pilot Andre Falconer who went out of his way to help, and to CareFlight management for its support and assistance.

Thanks to my large network of rural and remote friends and contacts for leading me to thirteen wonderful midwives.

Recommendations came in from all over Australia – the hardest part was keeping to just thirteen.

Thanks to associate publisher Jo Mackay, who had faith in my ability to write this book, my first, in a short timeframe. To editors Annabel, Alex and Laurie for their expertise, friendly assistance and guidance, and to all the team at Harlequin.

A huge thanks to my sister, Di Edwards, for reading through each chapter and offering seriously good advice and feedback. I thank author Sue Williams for her advice, kindness and encouragement.

To my husband Peter and daughter Ali; I owe them a great deal. To Matt and Natalia for cheering me on from a distance. And to my mother, Pat, who forgave my absences. And my brother Peter Walker, who is constantly there for me. Through some difficult months they all gave me the support and freedom I needed to write.

talk about it

Let's talk about books.

Join the conversation:

 on facebook.com/harlequinaustralia

 on Twitter @harlequinaus

www.harlequinbooks.com.au

If you love reading and want to know about our
authors and titles, then let's talk about it.